Sunset Across India

Susan Evans McCloud

BOOKCRAFT
Salt Lake City, Utah

Library of Congress Catalog Card Number: 95-80466
ISBN 1-57008-191-3

First Printing, 1995

Printed in the United States of America

To Pamela Morgan
dear friend and gracious spirit
I dedicate this book

Chapter One

The Hindu beliefs of my mother teach the law of *karma;* mainly, that every action, no matter how small, influences the state of the soul in its next incarnation. If a person performs honorably and lives a good life, his soul will be born into a higher state. And this, of course, is desirable. Therefore, one submits humbly to all afflictions of the current life that he might rise higher and live more comfortably in the next, until at last he achieves a spiritual perfection and enters that existence called *moksha* from which he need never return.

The Christian beliefs of my father teach that man must control mortal impulses and appetites and seek, through service and self-denial, that Christlike love and spiritual wholeness which will, at last, admit him to heaven when this life is past. He is to submit himself to the will of God and accept, humbly, whatever conditions, whatever trials and adversities may be imposed upon him for the sake of his learning and growth. Forbearance and submission are the watchwords.

So I had been taught. I never questioned; I never considered the possibility of any other manner of getting through life. And surely, nowhere on the globe is it easier to learn patience and forbearance than in the wild, exotic wastes of India. So I believed. So I had heard as a child growing up, from Constance and the other memsahibs, many dozens of times. I did not realize then how one-dimensional were the words and the beliefs which stood behind them. During a brief, condensed fragment of time I was to pass quickly—too quickly and too clumsily—from the serene, untried realm of childhood, where life is, by and large, theoretical and only vaguely understood, to the first threshold of womanhood and realization, and all the painful awareness, the giving up and the letting go, that come when one's eyes are open to see.

Major Reid's household, of which I was a part, was at present situated at Barrackpore, a military station on the banks of the Hooghly, sixteen miles from Calcutta along the Grand Trunk Road. This was in the year 1836 when a certain innocent belief in British supremacy, both among the Anglo-Indians and the natives, yet prevailed. Only the year before, English had been proclaimed the official language of the country, despite the fact that 180 different languages are spoken by the peoples of India—14 of them major tongues—not to mention the 700 minor dialects. But what was any of that? The army amassed by the East India Company, or merely John Company, as the British called it, numbered upwards of a quarter of a million men, only 15 percent of whom were Europeans. The British largely looked upon India as the "Land of Regrets," where they spent years of exile among a decadent, mysterious, sadly unenlightened people. Nevertheless, they were lords and masters there, entirely unintimidated and unimpressed by the hundreds of petty rajahs and princes still attempting to maintain their ancestral sway. British India *was* India, for all intents and purposes, more deeply and truly as each year passed.

The first small occurrence in the great chain of events that was to forever alter my life came on a day in mid-February, near the end of the cool, most pleasant—or least unpleasant—season in India. While speaking to the *malee,* or gardener, about the state of her nasturtiums, Constance fell into a swoon, for no apparent reason, and fainted dead away at the startled man's feet. This was not like Constance in the least. She was a healthy, well-fleshed woman of thirty-seven who had never indulged in the dull indolence, the empty, meaningless, almost hopeless existence which posed such a danger for British wives. Thrown upon her own resources, she had always found plenty to do, from raising money for charities and helping to found an orphanage, to sketching and painting, improving her needlework, and organizing amateur theatricals among the all-too-willing officers and their men. Her ingenuity and energy of spirit served her well, for in Indian life there is literally no work for a memsahib to do within her own household. A seemingly unending array of servants is provided to take care of the mistress's every possible need.

The major's staff of twenty-four included the boy (Sahib Reid's personal servant), the butler, the *hamal,* or housekeeper—whose major function was the ceaseless dusting and polishing of the memsahib's furniture. Then there was the *chupprassee,* or bodyguard; the *syce,* or groom; the cook; the *ayah*—who cared for the children with a tenderness which many of their own mothers lacked. The list continues, to include the milkman, the gardener, the *bheestee,* or water carrier, the *dirzee,* who was tailor and mender of clothes, the footmen and messengers, stewards and dishwashers—need I go on? Oh, yes, and the dog boy, whose sole purpose in life was to look after the family pet.

Nothing to do, indeed, for the confused English mistress save to control the servants, sort out their petty troubles and quarrels, and curb their consistent childlike offenses, which would prove so annoying to this cultured and educated master race.

So, this day, when Constance fainted, the whole household was set on edge. Once she had been safely carried to the long cushioned divan in the darkened sitting room, gently revived with smelling salts, propped with pillows, and served with a cup of strong tea, she sent away the dozen or more dark, dismayed faces with a decided clap of her hands, and suddenly no one was left in the room but the two of us.

She spoke without turning to face me. "You are seventeen, Charlotte, and old enough to be told such things. The reason I fainted . . . well . . ." Her firm, capable fingers fumbled at the light covering her maid had laid over her. "There is nothing the matter with me, really. It's just—you see, my dear, I am with child."

I stared at her dumbly. Somehow, that seemed to restore her. She laughed, almost indulgently. "It was a surprise to me, too."

"Are you certain?" I asked, without thinking. "Does the major know?"

"Yes to the first, dear, and no to the second." Her forehead wrinkled into creases of worry. "I cannot determine quite how to tell him." Her fingers fluttered again. She was not accustomed to feeling helpless or vulnerable; the state did not suit her well. "It is a bit shocking, isn't it? After all these years, Lottie. Roselyn would be sixteen, nearly your age; Arthur is twelve, Hugh ten." She threw up her arms in a gesture of dismay—awkward, but somehow endearing. "At my age, one would hardly expect—"

"Are you worried? Might it be dangerous for you?" I knew the question was too blunt and forward, but I had to know. Such as she was, Constance was the only mother I had any memory of. I was aware that my pulse was beginning to beat rather quickly and my throat had gone dry.

"Dr. Fielding does advise me to exercise caution and suggests that I give up my morning walk and anything at all requiring strenuous physical effort."

"You could take morning rides as most of the other ladies do."

"Yes." She spoke decidedly, as though she had already made up her mind. "And you shall canter alongside on Cinnamon to ward off any disturbance."

I smiled. Cinnamon was her horse, really, a gift from the major. But she had ridden the big chestnut gelding less than three times in the three years she had owned him. She had done little more than blight his life with the name she chose for him, then straightway ignored him, as she was wont to ignore anything she could not bend to her will and control to her liking. It became understood that the horse was mine in all save technical points of ownership, and that arrangement worked out to everyone's liking.

"We can do it," I encouraged, "make the adjustments we have to. It's for such a little while, really, and then . . ."

Constance attempted a smile. I had gone too far. "And then" implied the safe birth of a healthy baby. And here in India there was so much that could hamper or threaten that.

We pampered her for the remainder of the day. The boys' ayah kept them at a safe distance from her, and none of the servants were permitted to make the slightest disturbance. I thought to myself, *Constance will go mad after five days of this.* But I kept my own counsel and saw to it that cook prepared pullao rice and pork with bay leaves and coconut, her favorites. I also saw to it that she and the major were fairly deserted as soon as the meal was through. I smiled encouragingly as I turned my back on them. After all, Ralph Reid was not a difficult man to talk to. As I left the room I saw him push his fingers through the white hair at his temples and then lean slightly toward her. I covered the remaining distance as quietly as I could, and I did not look back.

I awoke the following morning at four-thirty, which is my habit. I washed and dressed quickly, then slipped through the darkened bungalow in search of Rosina, Constance's personal ayah, to see if memsahib was up. Rosina came down the hall with her finger to her lips, shushing me as she would one of the boys.

"The pork last night did not agree with her. She has been ill most of the night, but she is sleeping at last."

I stood blinking. "Is there anything I can do?" I blurted.

"Yes. You can go exercise that horse of yours and assure all the other memsahibs that Mrs. Reid is fine, nothing to worry."

I nodded and did as she told me. The morning was fair, with a cool, light mist rising off the river. Cinnamon pulled at the bit, little pleased with my slow gait. The small brown *bulbul* Rosina keeps as a pet trilled a cheery good morning as we cleared the yard, and fluttered its black-tipped wings at us. I began the long turn round the station, duly greeting the ladies who passed in their open carriages, parrying what questions were put to me and enjoying the semi-solitude which my perch atop Cinnamon's high back afforded. We cantered off the beaten path for a luxurious ten minutes, then headed back to the bungalow. The clean freshness of early morning had already begun to fade, to wilt under the promise of the day's heat rolling down upon us from a white, cloudless sky.

Breakfast was precisely at eight, as usual. I slid into my place one minute before the small Chippendale clock which sits on a shelf above the table began to strike the hour. Constance was not in her seat. I had not quite finished my mixture of eggs, anchovy, and yogurt, when Major Reid pushed back his chair and asked me to please join him in his office. I had not yet touched the small slices of fried bananas which are my favorite. But I rose immediately and followed him out.

As I entered the room he stood waiting for me, hands clasped behind his back. I knew at once this was serious; otherwise he would have sat in the tall leather chair behind his desk and settled in companionably, pipe in hand, for a long, pleasant chat. Instead, he paced the length of the small room thoughtfully, scarcely glancing at me.

"Alan—Dr. Fielding—has been here this morning, Lottie. It appears Constance may have a hard time of it."

"How is that, sir?" I asked cautiously. I had always called him "sir" or at times "Major Reid," never "Mr. Reid" or any title less formal. And though I called Constance by her given name, I nevertheless felt much more at ease, much more intimate with the major, and that had always confused me a little. In some ways it still did, though I had come to understand, after Roselyn's death, her mother's mixed feelings toward me, her difficulty in seeing me beside her, healthy and living, day after day, while her own flesh and blood—so protected, so cherished—lay in the parched clay of India, lost to her, lost to all the fond hopes she had held for her.

"She can hold down no food and complains of weakness and dizziness. She appears to be anemic, and the doctor fears jaundice or even a brain fever may threaten her if she is not under the most vigilant care."

I nodded. "I see. And that means . . ." He was obviously leading to something. He threw me a grateful glance and sighed.

"The boys must be sent back to England, to school. Constance has a sister in Devonshire who will see to them." He rubbed his clasped hands together in an agitated manner. "Dash it all, Lottie, it's high time anyway, now, isn't it? Most of the lads hereabout go back before they reach Hugh's age, and Arthur's a big boy of twelve. They ought to get along, the both of them together."

His bluster was a poor cover for his distress, which I knew was as painful as mine.

"You're perfectly right, of course. The boys are splendid and well trained. They'll manage." I stepped up close to him and laid my hand on his arm. "And so shall we, sir. We'll help one another."

He covered my hand with one of his and his round face softened. "Yes, my dear, what would we do without you?"

It was at such moments as these that I felt truly loved, truly at ease in the world, and content with my lot, despite the fact that both my own parents were lost to me.

"Will you tell them?" he asked.

My eyes widened; I could feel my expression alter.

"Come, you'd do a much better job of it. You know I'm capable of botching the whole thing miserably."

I planted a kiss on his cheek. His eyes, as soft and expressive as a woman's, reflected the gratitude it was not necessary for him to speak.

"I'll take care of it. Have you any engagements this evening?"

"Blast it. I'm afraid that I do." He moved toward the door, his thoughts shifting onto the day's responsibilities. "Perhaps I can beg off, considering . . ."

"Is the station to be told, then, of . . ." I hesitated, realizing for the first time that he had said nothing, given no indication of his own feelings concerning Constance's announcement, concerning the impending arrival of an unexpected addition to his family. "Are you disturbed, sir, about—well, the baby?"

He regarded me thoughtfully for a moment, the kind eyes clouding. "Well, actually, yes, Lottie, I am a bit. After all, at my age one is hardly expecting . . . there's a certain awkwardness to it."

I nodded, understanding enough to appreciate his position and moved, as always, by his honesty, his explicit trust in me.

"Then there's the other as well." He added this softly, his eyes on the rug at his feet. "Nothing must happen to this child, nothing must go wrong. I don't know if Constance could bear it."

"Yes," I replied. "Yes, I've already thought of that, too."

He glanced at the oval mahogany clock that sat on his desk. "Well, the lads are expecting me. Busy day ahead."

He began to move past me in that deliberate, shuffling gait of his. But he paused long enough to plant a kiss on the top of my head. "Good luck with the boys and all that," he said, and I knew that he meant it.

"Thank you," I replied. "Don't worry. We'll manage; we'll all manage just fine."

I waited until the boys' morning lessons were over, and instead of sending their ayah away, I took them with me to the park, lamenting too late that their boyish glee at the prospect of an outing must be thoughtlessly and unavoidably dampened. I found myself postponing the inevitable moment, allowing the children to romp unchecked along the broad paths, beneath the shade of the banyan, shisham and nim trees, and a whole line of poinsettias that stood nearly fifteen feet high. A breeze with a bit of coolness still in it breathed over the jasmine and myrtle and set the slender bamboo stalks rasping. I shuddered and called the boys to me with a firmness in my voice that brought them tumbling helter-skelter, nearly on top of one another, like two frisky puppies.

I bade them sit at my feet and explained first the more delicate portion of my assignment. Their mother having a baby!

Hugh stared wide-eyed, but Arthur dropped his gaze to study the toe of his boot and muttered, "I don't believe you! I thought only young women had babies. Mother's too old. It isn't . . . proper!"

He spat the last word out as his neck grew a deep shade of red. I replied matter-of-factly, "She is a bit old, Arthur, and that is why we're concerned for her." I tried to keep a delicate balance. "And yet women her age have babies successfully; it is not uncommon. She must receive proper care. We must each do everything in our power . . ."

He squinted up at me, still not quite meeting my eyes. "And what does that mean for Hughie and me?"

I drew a deep breath. "It means school in England," I replied, determined to treat them with the same candid courtesy their father had shown to me. I forced a lightness into my voice. "I know. It's something you've both dreaded and looked forward to—the great adventure and the fearful unknown. Well, now it is here."

"Davey Chandler went when he was only eight," Hugh offered, his mouth set in a determined line that made me think suddenly of his mother.

"Yes, and the Sullivan boy was just your age when he left last fall."

Arthur was thinking. He was slow and methodical, a bit like his father. When at last he spoke it was with that same cautious, considered air, and it tugged at my heartstrings.

"We must do our duty and not add to Father's burdens by vexing him."

I nodded, equally solemn.

"I'll look out for Hugh." He placed a hand on his brother's knee. "I suppose we'll be sent to Aunt Alice's, first at least. Has Father decided upon a school yet?"

"I don't believe so," I answered honestly. How thorough his young mind was!

"I wish *you* could go with us." Hugh's brave resolve was crumpling. I wanted to stretch my arms out and draw him close against me.

"That *would* be nice. I've not seen England, and I'm never likely to do so."

"Well, when I'm grown to a man that's where I shall live, Lottie, and I'll send for you, and you shall stay as long as you like."

I gave him a wavering smile. "Very well. I shall hold you to that."

I let them talk the thing over and over, examining all sides, all possibilities of the new life which was to be suddenly thrust upon them. By the time we rose on stiff legs we were all quite buoyed up with courage, resolve, and a high curiosity. That is how it should be. I was not one capable of calling their attention to the true realities which might await them. If that was cowardly of me, or even somewhat dishonest, so let it be. Hope is a fine weapon with which to combat the struggles of life. Without it a man believes himself nothing, and the colors of the universe fade into a stark, hueless gray which mocks his very existence. So I remember thinking as we walked out of the gardens, hand in hand, the three of us. And so I was to recall not too many months later, as I gazed into another young face, as earnest, as etched with fear and uncertainty as the boys' faces had been that day.

Chapter Two

What was quickly decided upon was put into quick execution. Within a fortnight the major had obtained passage for the two boys in company with a fellow officer who, recovering from a battle with malaria, was now being sent home. I think it was better that way, for all of us. It was the contemplation of the prospect before us that hurt, that tattered our patience and drew out the threads of our tenderness until each day that we waited and anticipated, gazing into the bright, lovely faces of the children, was like a small death in itself.

Constance said little. I had thought she might grow surly, even demanding, and send for the boys often, weighing them down with the burden of her motherly fussing and fears. It was not so. She came as close to ignoring them as seemed decently possible. I disguised this as well as I could by a pretended aggravation of the complaints she was suffering, and an increase in my own attentions toward them. Poor little things. Their days were filled with fair and useful employment, their minds kept busy and active, but what of their hearts? What of the silent hours they lay in their darkened bedroom staring into the night? Were they able to stare down their own fears and uncertainties, or simply hold them at bay?

Their clothes were in readiness, along with the few personal possessions they were being allowed to take with them. Another three weeks passed before the date for departure of the vessel came round. A correspondence had already been sent off to Aunt Alice, who hopefully would receive it before the boys themselves should arrive. They were assured dozens of times of the good lady's kindness and of her willingness to care for them and oversee their education, being a maiden aunt with no children of her own. But as the dread day approached, the boys grew a bit pale and listless and their appetites flagged. The flesh on the major's big face seemed to sag and his eyes looked pale and irritated, as though he had taken to rubbing them quite a lot. Radha, the boys' ayah, revealed nothing of her feelings, unless one looked into her eyes. They had been like her own children to her, received into her keeping when they were only days old. Her quiet spirit had moulded them in ways their parents would never know. She went about her tasks with the same patient efficiency, but her olive eyes, deep-set and veiled, yet revealed the terrible suffering she endured.

The little Englishmen, I thought to myself, *are expected to be stoic like their father, to keep a stiff upper lip. How many times have I heard the major say that? So they push their emotions away. On the other hand, the Indian covers his emotions also, with layers of calm, with a silken acceptance, a pretense as careful, as false in its way as the Englishman's.* And where was I? *Where do I fit in?* I asked myself.

Seldom before had I given much thought to my differences. Indeed, I was scarcely aware of them. Why should I be? I knew nothing but this life. I was as much an Englishwoman, a missysahib, as any other; in fact, in some obvious ways, I was more skilled than most. Thanks to Constance I could play the piano and stitch a fine seam. I knew food and what was considered proper nutrition, the ordering of meals, the organizing of the household along the lines of wise economy and strict control. I was an excellent horsewoman and a rather fine dancer. But, more than that, I was acquainted with the best in literature and poetry; indeed, I could recite many pieces from memory. I knew history and, thanks to the major, a spattering of philosophy which could spark my conversation whenever that need arose. There was little, really, I could not turn my hand to. "You have done us both proud," Major Reid was in the habit of saying. But, whenever he did, Constance would smile vaguely and then look away from us. And we were both meant, myself in particular, to understand and, therefore, excuse her. How could she help but think of her own dead daughter at such times as these?

Constance was no better. She was not pretending the effort it took her to rise from her sickbed to see the boys off. In the end there were tears and smothering caresses; of course there would be. Once or twice I saw Arthur's chin tremble, but no tear shamed his eye. Poor Hugh gave up the effort at last and hid his face in my skirts. Major Reid shook their hands, small and cold against his, and in the end pulled them roughly into his arms. They marched onto the ship with the air of young martyrs. I turned away quickly, unable to watch, skuttling like any coward back to see to their mother, who began to chatter vaguely about the rent that the carriage wheel had torn in her gown, and had I remembered to inform cook that her tamarind chicken had tasted tainted last night, and she was not to purchase fowl one more time from that cousin of hers or she would find herself summarily dismissed and no amount of tears would avail her—and, oh, had we taken note of Captain Hall at the docks, and who was that smart-looking young woman who clung to his arm?

All the way back to the bungalow it was the same mindless chatter, until my nerves were worn thin. Not until I helped her into bed did I notice how cold her skin was, and how empty her eyes.

We had missed the *basant,* the day in late February when the fields are covered with yellow mustard bloom and the children fly kites, and all rejoice by wearing clothes of soft yellow and eating sweet yellow rice. We had missed the March festival of *Holi,* the day of many colors when children are allowed to play tricks and make mischief to their young hearts' content. We had missed *Navroze,* the spring festival celebrated on

March 21, when all the homes, freshly cleaned, are bedecked with spring flowers, fragrant and dripping with color, and families feast and give thanks. There are so many holidays, festivals, and holy fairs in India, literally hundreds in number. They punctuate the dreariness of daily life for the people. They create beauty and hope, and they keep remembrance alive.

But the British have no real part in them, except to either scoff or admire at a distance. The races of India have so little in common with the English, whose civilized pleasures include cricket and tennis, cards or billiards after supper, formal dinners and nearly as formal dances for which they dress in clothes that stifle the spirit as well as the flesh which must endure them. But then there is horse racing. That alone, to my way of thinking, brings men together, men of all backgrounds, both religious and racial, with one common feeling and one common delight. So I could observe. But I always observed as an *Englishwoman.* This was my country, but in what way? In the way of the outsider, the conquerer, the usurper? In the way of the natives who, though they had been here forever, were giving way before change?

We had been absorbed these past weeks in Constance's illness and plans for the boys' departure. And the sameness of our days had become intolerable. Now that Hugh and Arthur were gone we at first felt ourselves cast adrift, gazing into a great emptiness with no idea of how we might fill it.

Constance decided, during those first uncommon days, that she would keep the boys' ayah on, trusted as she was, so that she would be in place to take care of the infant when it was born. No gender was ever assigned the poor growing creature. If it turned out a boy, things would go well enough for it. But, if a girl—if a girl it would very likely be held up as some sort of miracle, another chance, even a kind of reincarnation of the happy days that had been.

Constance's friends, by and large, were wise women. As soon as the boys departed they began quietly to fill up the void. They talked her into lying in state in the drawing room during receiving hours, late morning through early afternoon.

Careful to not overtax her, they held planning meetings in her presence, assigning some little task for the next ball or charity project or bazaar that she would be able to do. They brought out their yarns and laces and began fashioning baby clothes for the expected one. They drank gallons of tea and summed up dozens of reputations with the fine, critical mesh of their talk.

For my own part, there was still precious little to occupy me. I took longer rides on Cinnamon, morning and evening, when such were permitted and feasible. I indulged my bent for reading and scribbling maudlin lines of poetry. I planned and replanned meals, I oversaw the work in the gardens. Oh, yes, and I dutifully played with the boys' monkey, Mischief, as I had promised, though I thought him a spoiled, dirty thing. I was in danger, at least for the first few days, of giving into that inertia they wryly call "Sand in the Head," that terrible boredom which can strike and destroy English women, stuck like so many prisoners on their desert outposts, with a sure and disarming deadliness. But I was young. Young and spirited, and that was in my favor.

I had been thinking much about Roselyn since the boys' departure to England. I enjoyed recalling the days when we two were the children, the little ones, running untamed and willful, setting the household on end. We *had* been willful, as only spoiled little girls can be. Much that we indulged in could be classified as common to most curious and healthy children: ditching lessons to play with our dolls in the tall, sweet grasses that border the river; cajoling cook into letting us help in the kitchen, and then not only ruining the beef bandaloo beyond recognition but spoiling our good frocks as well; catching and containing an entire colony of lizards—green and specked and mottled brown as an old twig—and convincing ourselves that we had trained them to do tricks for us and to not mind the leashes we tugged them around on.

On the side of originality was the time we took the old cat's whole litter of kittens, eight strong, dressed them in our dolls' clothes, and sold them door to door through the compound. Then, overcome with the magnificence of our earnings, we hitched a ride with a family of villagers that happened to be passing, crowding into their oxcart amongst half a dozen round-faced children, until we reached the main street of the village, where we spent every last one of our precious coins buying sweets from the *mit hai wala,* whose small booth opened right onto the street and who seemed to be frying his *jalebis* and *gulab jamans* for us alone. My, we were the sick ones! All white-faced and sticky-fingered, with a terrible pain in our stomachs when we decided we'd best start out and try to find our way home. We walked until our feet were more sore than our middles. Roselyn was crying when old Domingo, one of the house servants on his way to the village, found us. He had meant to pay a visit to his sister who was ill, but instead he turned his small cart around and drove us back home. He was not pleased. His sister was the best cook in Nepal and Bengal put together, sick or not sick. He felt we had cheated him sorely. Of course, Constance was as mad as a wet hen. I remember it well. I was seven years old and had been living two years with the major's family. She could still frighten me, but I was beginning to trust Major Reid's compassionate nature and complacent attitude toward childish offenses.

And, of course, it was easy to assign the larger portion of blame to the unnatural daughter. I was, in truth, the bolder and more aggressive. Roselyn possessed her father's caution as well as an open and good disposition, also inherited from him. She could not be "bad" in the sense that some children are. I never remember a time when we two were nasty and vindictive with each other as young girls can be. Perhaps she was too good for this earth, perhaps God did take her away and plant her in a happier garden than can grow in our dry Indian soil.

One morning in early April I found myself heading Cinnamon toward the cemetery, drawn by a growing need to stand before the small mound of earth where my dead playmate lay. It was very early still and the paths were empty; only the grave markers rose, close and cramped, crowded against one another. The English dead claimed an impressive portion of Indian soil for their inheritance. Poor inheritance, this. I moved quickly past the row, tidy and even, of five little headstones where five Henderson children rested close beside one another, the oldest but six. An angel of mercy spread her stone wings above them. Perhaps she was meant to be smiling, but it seemed she was weeping to me. I always fancied I could hear the sound of her lamenting, much like the rush of many birds' wings, soft and feathered above me.

I tethered Cinnamon to a post, leaving her to enjoy the tall grasses that grew along the pathway, and proceeded on foot. When my mother died, Major Reid and my father, both captains then, had been stationed in Lucknow, but were in Baraset when my father went off in search of the annihilation which mercifully found him. We had been in Barrackpore less than a year when Roselyn was forced to make her final home here. After that, the major received "emergency" permission to maintain this post, though he often traveled extensively with his unit. But Constance always remained. Indeed, the first few years following Roselyn's death she could not even be persuaded to make the journey up to Simla to escape the madness of the heat and the monsoon season.

I pushed my way through the dense growth, aware suddenly that it had been a long time since my last visit here. The smell of roses and jasmine was suddenly too close, too heavy. I knelt on the ground. There before me, etched into a slab of pink marble, rosy and gray in the white light, I read her name—"Roselyn May Reid"—with the dates carved beneath it, and then this line: "She rests now with the fair ones of heaven, but we envy the angels who enjoy her company and gaze on her face." A very Constanceish emotion. Here there was no "rest in peace," but a quiet anger I could feel, almost directed at Roselyn for going away.

She had been a fair one. Round-faced and soft-skinned like her father, with soft, doe-like eyes, and soft hair that always seemed to be lifting, floating with the slightest stir of the air. Her hair was not gold, but it seemed to have gold threads woven through it, just enough to lend her an appearance of light and beauty which her features were a little too ordinary, a little too weak, too rounded, to do by themselves.

We used to sit side by side on the vanity stool together, gazing into the mirror. Even then I was aware of how her features complemented the rose and mauve and blue ribbons Constance bought for our hair. My eyes stared back at me, not black like the natives', but dark like the wet brown of tree bark, with green flecks visible in them when the lighting was right; hair not sleek and black, but showing rich streaks of auburn and its own stubborn curl, despite the thick, heavy length of it. My father had red-blonde curls that covered his head and hugged his neckline, and green eyes as sharp as a cat's, and a sharp, thin nose, but a full, laughing mouth. I don't really remember, but I have been told thus when I pestered so with my questions that I could not be denied. All I remember is that he seemed a young god to me. I liked the feel of his hands when they lifted me, and the sound of his voice, and the smell of him, lime with a mingling of cardamom, ginger, and cloves.

I was not aware of the soldier until I heard a cough directly behind me, a small, purposeful sound. I turned my head slowly, reluctant to let go of the solitude I thought had been mine.

The man I saw framed against the delicate lacing of banyan branches appeared to be tall and slender, though the Company uniform had the tendency to flatter the lines of most men. His face was angular, with strong lines and a firm chin, and a finely shaped nose. His eyes were almond-shaped and set deep in his face under dark, penciled brows. He had a thick thatch of black hair that his squat, loose-fitting hat could not entirely conceal. And he was a sepoy, a native soldier, the flesh of his face as brown as a ginger root.

He folded his hands together and bowed respectfully. "*Namaste*," he said, which interpreted means, "I bow my head to you."

I bowed in return.

"I have disturbed you," he murmured. The words were an

apology. His voice was deep-toned and resonant, yet with that curious sense of silence, of underlying harmony which some Indians have.

"It is of no matter," I replied.

"But it is. She is someone dear to you?"

I stared down at the grave marker and nodded.

"Of course!" His uneasiness was growing. He sighed and glanced around him, as though wishing for a means of escape. I felt moved to rescue him.

"Have you also come to pay homage to one who is among the dead?"

"A fellow officer, only a boy when he came here—a younger son who could win no higher commission." His broad shoulders beneath the heavy uniform jacket shrugged slightly. "I befriended him. We were much alike in some ways. But he died of the malaria when he had been but six months in India."

"What a sad waste," I muttered.

"Indeed. There are many sad ways of wasting a life."

I glanced at him more closely. He was handsome in that dark, quiet, almost mysterious way which is so common to the men of his race. But there was something more, something about the way his eyes looked at me, and the things that he said.

"The young girl who rests at your feet, was she—"

"My sister," I replied, then found myself stuttering, "Well, not really my sister. We lived as sisters, though we were in no real way related—and there were two little brothers as well, very dear to me. They've just been sent back to England for schooling, and I suppose I'm feeling a bit sorry for myself, and lonely."

He waved my clumsy protest aside. "Brother and sister, a precious and sacred relationship—at least among my people."

I could see that he was studying me closely, confused by my unusual looks and complexion, wondering and, therefore, uncertain.

"Each year we celebrate the festival called *Raksha Bandhan*. On this day a girl fastens the *rakhi*, or bracelet, over her brother's wrist and he promises to protect and help her if she is ever in need."

"I did not know that."

His eyes grew very gentle. "A boy who has not been blessed with a sister is often adopted by a female cousin, for it is a trust to be desired, this caring, this protecting of a woman."

His voice moved over my skin like a caress. I felt myself shudder and turned my eyes away from him. He sensed my discomfort; I could feel that he did.

He kicked with the toe of his boot at the torn red petals of the semal tree that littered the ground at our feet. The birds had dropped them there, tearing apart the heavy scarlet blooms for the honey that sweetens their hearts.

I took a few steps away from him, toward the broad path where Cinnamon waited. "I had better be going," I said.

He backed away, bowing slightly in deference. I passed very close to him, but did not glance back. I mounted my horse and began to move out of the graveyard. But, after covering only a yard or two, I felt a fierce pain in my hand—a hot pain that shot up my arm like a fire. I heard my own voice cry out, then bit my lip against the pain and felt myself sway in the saddle.

I watched the scurrying brown insect move over the leather pommel where, moments before, my hand had rested—a small brown scorpion, perhaps four inches long. I thought vaguely, as through a mist, *At least it is not seven inches long and black in color. I can endure this.*

But the pain was increasing. My whole arm was beginning to throb, and there was a high, thin singing inside my head.

He had come up beside me without my noticing. Through the wavering mist I watched him tie Cinnamon's long lead rein to something at the back of his saddle. Then his arms were at my waist and he was lifting me gently, and the world started swimming, earth and sky blending together into a sickening green. I tried to smile, I tried to speak. He put his hand on my forehead and it felt cool against my flesh.

"Where do you live?" he asked. "Where can I take you?"

"Major Reid . . . Ralph Reid . . ." My tongue felt thick in my mouth and the words seemed to slur.

But he nodded, and then pulled me against him, and I realized I was sitting in front of him on his horse, my head resting on his shoulder, the pain wrenching through me in great crimson waves. That was the last I remembered with any degree of coherency.

Together the servants must have got me into my bed. I wonder if the quiet sepoy, strong of arm and efficient, helped. Several servants brought herbs and home remedies to apply to the sting, but nothing seemed to make any difference. I believe someone sent for Dr. Fielding, but he could not be found.

"Twenty-four hours," my ayah pronounced, with the weight of a sentence. "After that, the poison will pass, and the pain along with it."

I tried to smile up into her wrinkled brown face. Vijaya had been with me since before I could remember; it was her hand I held tightly to when I first entered Major Reid's house. She had been nursemaid to both myself and Roselyn—nursemaid, teacher, friend, and advisor; and mother to me. Part of me had always realized that she was more mother than Constance knew how to be.

Though I slept not a wink during that long, torturous night, Vijaya had the right of it. The pain disappeared all of a sudden, in much the way that it came. I was weak and worn out with the force of it, but the nightmare was done.

I felt a certain restlessness the evening following my recovery, and did not wish to admit that it could have anything to do with the young sepoy who had come to my aid. But because of it I bathed and dressed myself with more care than usual and ordered the servants to saddle my mount. In India each individual horse has two servants—one to prepare his food and feed him, the other to groom and clean him.

The sun had gone down. If not genuine coolness, at least

the promise of it softened the air like a scent. I rode down the mall at a slow, casual pace, glancing about me, from side to side, not too obviously I hoped. The Indian soldier was an officer; I had seen that from the insignia which his uniform bore. But he was a native and, therefore, not part of society, and the social orders were most severe here. Strict observance of these orders meant that ladies of Constance's social level did not acknowledge those beneath them, who were referred to as "women" and seldom mixed with at all. And, of course, with the men the order was just as exacting. It did not matter to me, these petty observances. I wanted to see my benefactor again, I wanted to thank him; I did not even yet know his name.

He was not there. I rode round and round till my spirits dampened and I felt wilted and deflated and the music the band was playing throbbed painfully in my head. When at last I returned in defeat to the bungalow, I was more than surprised to encounter Constance dressed for the evening and pacing the length of the sitting room.

"Have you forgotten the dance at the Club this evening?" Her question was itself a biting accusation. "I wondered if you would feel up to attending, but since you've been out riding . . ." She left the sentence hanging in mid-air.

"And yourself?" I turned the question back upon her.

"I shall stay only a short while." She sighed. "The evening is lovely and these four walls are beginning to fold in upon me." She fluttered her hands in the new way she had acquired. Suddenly my heart went out to her, and feeling ashamed of my meanness, I planted a kiss on her cheek.

"By all means, I shall be happy to accompany you, Constance, and make the evening as enjoyable for you as I can." I put my hand to my hair, loosened and disheveled by my ride. "Ten minutes with Vijaya's help and I shall be ready," I promised, and I was rewarded by one of her rare, even grateful, smiles.

My restlessness continued throughout the evening, despite my attempts to curb it or will it away. The stiff formality, the shallow politeness, the measured strains of the waltzes and quadrilles had an effect upon me that was nauseating. I watched the formal order of ladies being led in proper keeping with their station and that of their husbands. And when a particularly pleasant young captain approached me, his blue eyes sparkling, and asked for a dance, something came over me. For the remainder of the evening I behaved shamefully, I must admit it—just like one of the "fishing fleet," those vapid young women with white skin and big eyes who arrived at our posts via ships in search of one thing: men. Husbands—any kind of husband, particularly an older one with some money and security. But the favored few, the younger men with looks and manners and some promise of a future, how eagerly they were assailed!

Well, I joined in the flirting and enjoyed every murmur and blush of it—as well as the disconcerted reactions of some of the startled young ladies who suddenly fancied me a rival. In my contrariness I enjoyed their discomfort, and it pleased me to see that the captain's obvious favorites were myself and young Gwen Abbott, the prettiest woman on base. The prettiest, but already taken. Did the elegant captain know that? I wondered, and the wondering only added to the excitement that throbbed through the air.

Nevertheless, I was grateful for the excuse to beg off early and take Constance home. The major stayed, of course; but he could be trusted. Unlike many of the officers, he had never behaved unseemly with the women, never taken an Indian mistress—and I'm certain he had had his share of chances. He was attractive in his own way; women found him so, with his thick black hair graying only at the forehead and temples, and the sincerity of his gallantry mingled with the warmth of his gaze. I wondered, as he gave Constance a peck on the cheek and patted my head, if the union between them had been a good one, satisfying for him.

The image of the sepoy's face came into my mind unbidden, and I shook it away, kissing my hand to the young gentlemen who looked after me ruefully, and catching the captain's bold eye, stunned, but also delighted by the boldness of the message I read in his gaze.

Chapter Three

I WENT TO THE CEMETERY THE SECOND TIME for one purpose, and one alone. I did bring a nosegay of flowers to set atop Roselyn's grave. But after placing them there, I walked to where the banyan tree, its trunks wrinkled and intertwined, spread its immense fairy canopy, like the tracery of the gods, across the expanse of blue sky. And I waited, my eyes closed, listening to the rooks' cries as they swooped overhead; and the wild loneliness of their call sent shivers along my skin.

The sun warmed my eyelids. I was vaguely aware of a small green lizard who, having made his way across the rough bark, was now attempting my arm, but unsure of the soft feel of flesh beneath his toes. I did not hear the movement of a horse, I did not hear footsteps as he approached. It was his voice that startled me to open my eyes wide and stare at him.

"Have you a certain attraction, is it the scent of your skin, that draws these creatures to crawl on you?"

He spoke in a light tone, teasing, but not presumptuous; he did not mean to bait me in any way. With a flick of his finger he sent the lizard scurrying. His finger remained; then he shifted and lightly rested his hand on my arm.

"You are recovered?" He lifted my wrist to examine the angry red swelling where the insect had stung.

"Yes, much better." I drew in my breath. The warmth of his touch still lingered. "I have been looking for you, to thank you."

"That is not necessary." His voice had dropped, and I could not read his expression.

"But what is your name? I did not even know what to call you."

He smiled. My words were, in a way, ridiculous, as both of us knew. Call him, name him, to whom? There was no instance when the need would arise for me to refer to him, not in the company I kept.

I must have sighed. He put a finger under my chin, raising the level of my gaze to meet his. "I am Karan," he said, "and you are Charlotte. And it was a favor of the gods that I was here that day to help you."

Why was I drawn to him so? Why did something familiar and sweet course through me at the sight of his face? Why did his voice sound like a caress? Why did my fingers ache to reach up and touch his smooth cheek?

"Nevertheless . . ." I paused. I could not dissemble, could neither be coy nor pretentious, not with this man. "Nevertheless, I wanted to see you, Karan, be with you again."

He understood. He understood so perfectly that the knowledge of his knowing seared through me when I looked into his eyes.

"Are you certain of this, Charlotte?"

I met his gaze levelly. "Yes. We can be friends."

"We cannot be friends, and well you know it. You are not being wise."

"But I am not being willful, either. I mean no harm, I have no hidden motive."

He was shaking his head.

"The system and society which prohibits us this innocent pleasure is not of our making," I pressed. "There is something that brought us together—you feel it."

He lowered his eyes. For a moment the silence sat heavy between us. Then he spoke, and his words were like so many sad little stones. "For your sake I should deny you, Charlotte." He drew my name out until the syllables trembled. "But for your sake, I will stay."

We talked. There was no barrier of custom or background between us, no awkward constraints. Time ceased to exist. After a while, as if by unspoken agreement, we parted. I rode to the bungalow, aware of a sense of well-being, similar to the way one feels when one's health is good, one's mind clear, one's senses unclouded, and the weather invigorating—all things in tune. I greeted Constance, who was reclining in the cool, darkened sitting room. I felt no sense of guilt; rather, refined and refreshed, as though I had drunk from some sweet spring, pure and inviolable—and mine alone.

We had already hung the tatties, curtains of reeds and dry grasses which are kept wet during the hot hours and have a surprisingly cooling effect on the rooms they serve. The white ants were out en masse, destroying woodwork, picture frames, fine inlaid tables and boxes, even paper, if it is left too long unattended. Millipedes and the pale, bloodless crickets scuttered across the floors. The mosquitoes would come later with the monsoon rains. This hot, breathless season dried up everything but the insects. Nothing had the power to destroy or diminish them.

Many of the women and their households had already left for Simla, the retreat at the foot of the Himalayas that the British had created to serve their sanity and, at the same time, satisfy their senses. But Constance demurred. I knew she dreaded the nearly thousand mile journey that must be endured to get there. But the alternative, the prospect of staying, was worse—now, and more so once the rains struck.

At last I was able to write to Arthur and Hugh:

Dear Brothers,

We leave for Simla next week. Here the flowers curl and burn brown in the sun, and the clicking of the punkahs, the splash and dripping of water against the tatties, can be heard day and night.

Your wretched monkey persists in tearing up the gardens, finding always the choicest young fruits and vegetables to devour. I believe he is bored without your company, and mischief is the only outlet for his energies.

They knew my distaste of the beastie and would only be delighted to read of his antics and offenses.

I cannot imagine this England where you are. Your mother describes it: wet—consistently wet, but never excessively as here. Green, with narrow, cobbled lanes and small, thatch-roofed cottages. Cozy, with everything close together, like a miniature kingdom. She says I would miss the sun. Do you? Do you miss the camels and elephants? Write and tell me about it.

Young boys are not good correspondents. We had received only one communication from them since they had left. It had been short and straightforward, and I was not able to read much between the lines. Nor had I been encouraged by their Aunt Anne's response to their arrival. A maiden lady used to silence and the idiosyncrasies of her own way of living could not be expected to adjust with ease to the sudden presence of two noisy, rambunctious boys. And besides, she was Constance's sister—that made her suspect enough.

At last we were going to Simla. And best of all, Karan would be traveling with us. I had learned that glowing fact only a few days before. Our meetings had now reached the grand number of seven, most taking place in the cemetery beneath the shade and protection of the old banyan tree. It is strange how much two people just recently acquainted can manage to say to each other. We talked and talked and never grew weary, nor ran out of things to talk about. He was a Sikh from the Punjab. The Sikhs are by and large tall, handsome men; excellent fighters, tenacious and loyal, but with a fire in them which at times can leap and burn out of control. I did not see any of this fire in Karan; he kept it well in control. I saw only his tenderness, his respect for emotion, his fine, tutored mind. He had been educated at some of the earliest schools in Calcutta, as well as in the language and religion of his own people.

"You move well in both worlds," I told him. "How do you do that?"

"Compromise," he replied in a sad tone, "and self-denial."

And at that moment I knew that his discipline, his incredible hold on himself was for my sake alone.

"The major does not accompany us to Simla," I informed him. "He will come later, for the birth of the child, since he must—"

"Is that the way in which Major Reid views it?" he asked. His face was inscrutable.

"Yes, to a degree. English men and women are kept far removed from one another where such things are concerned. He is busy, and he is afraid. If something were to happen to Constance—or, worse, to the child, well . . ." I did not know how to say it.

"He runs away in his way, as she does in hers."

"Yes. That is at least partially true. Yes, I suppose in some ways he does." I looked at him carefully. I wanted to know what he was thinking. "But the Englishman, you see, is not trained for any other kind of behavior."

"Does nothing come naturally to him?" There was an edge to his voice. "If this were my wife and my child . . ."

But his eyes said: *If this were you and me, Charlotte.* His eyes had never yet been so bold.

He turned the subject, but only a little. "You are not as these Englishwomen. You have other blood in your veins."

I swatted angrily at a tight clump of leaves that hung in front of me. "Yes, but of what good is that? I have been raised up as the English are raised, with only that side of me fostered. And as to the rest . . ."

I hesitated. I could tell that my eyes were smouldering, my lips beginning to tremble. "I have no knowledge of my mother. I do not know her origin, what people she came from."

He could hear the tears in my voice and reached for my

hand, which I gave him. "She looks out from your eyes."

I smiled a bit ruefully. "That sounds very lovely, poetic."

"Especially since it is true."

I moved my head in a quick, impatient gesture and pulled my hand out of his grasp.

"Spirit can be passed on, as well as characteristics of the flesh. Hers is strong in you, part of what renders you like no other."

I bit my lip. "No two people, Karan, are ever alike."

He refused to be baited. "Yes, and in all the millions of people who swarm over the world, only a choice few stand out. You know this, and I know this . . . and you understand well what I say."

I dropped my eyes. "What am I? Never before have I longed so fiercely to know who I am!"

His sympathy reached out to me, as rich with tenderness as though my pain were his own.

"Perhaps that is why we have found one another."

"That reason alone?"

He said nothing; again he refused to be drawn by me.

"Though we travel to Simla in the same company," I said, "there will be much confusion, and many hundreds of people—"

"You mean there will be order, and you shall have your place, and I have mine."

"Yes, that is what I mean." I sighed. Perhaps I should have felt foolish, but I did not at all.

"I may actually see less of you there than—than we are accustomed . . ."

I could feel him relenting at last. "I have thought of this also. I am not looking forward . . ."

I moved, simply leaning my body closer to his. The foliage whispered, then the whole world held still.

"No, Charlotte! It would prove more curse than blessing if I were to . . ."

His voice was trembling, and there was a note of appeal to it which I had never yet heard.

I lifted my face. His fingers reached out until the very tips of them touched my cheek. I was pleading with him, though only silently in my heart. There was no word spoken, no sound. After a long time he moved, bent above me like a warm, fragrant shadow, and placed his lips over mine. And in that meeting, that coming together, I knew not only the acute pleasure of the flesh, but a sensation of joy—my joy and his, a mingling that felt as sweet, as natural as his kiss.

What twisted sense of the dramatic, what cruel delight do the fates take in tormenting humankind? It was this day, when I rode home through the gathering dusk and entered the darkened bungalow, that the major was waiting.

He was not a timid man, but his own kindness distressed him. But, be that as it may, he went straight to the point.

"One of my officers has brought it to my attention, Lottie, that he has seen you several times in the company of a young sepoy. In fact, only last night, coming out of the cemetery—"

"How does he know we were in one another's company?" I could feel my breath tighten painfully within me.

"Were you, my dear?"

"Yes, we were. Yes, I know the man. He is an officer, sir—he is the one who came to my assistance, quite inadvertently, when the scorpion stung me."

"I see." He looked a bit relieved. "Then you did not seek this acquaintance."

"No, but I have encouraged it." The words fell individually into the quiet room like a death knell.

"My dear, that is very unwise."

"I do not see why. He is refined and gentlemanly, and his integrity can be trusted without question." I spoke slowly, in a soft, reasonable voice. Nevertheless, he reached out and placed his hand over mine.

"That makes it worse, Lottie, you know. What of the danger, the very real danger of your growing too fond of him?"

What could I answer? I dropped my eyes and let him squeeze the hand that lay under his.

"Well, well." He patted the hand in his effort to convince

himself that all would be well. "You leave for the mountains in three days. If I have your word that you will not see him again before your departure, then we will table the whole affair for the time being."

I gave him my word.

"Good," he replied, patting my hand again. "Very well, Lottie. Now we must discuss Constance and what measures can be taken for her maximum comfort and safety. It's very good of you to shoulder the entire responsibility, you know, until I arrive."

I nodded. *Very good indeed,* I thought. It was painfully evident to me that the major saw no discrepancy here, no sad irony. He was willing to allow me responsibility for his entire household, and the well-being of his wife, whose physical *and* mental states were both precariously unstable. In that he did not question my ability nor my maturity. But where my own life was concerned, the reasonings of my mind and the perceptions of my heart, he still perceived me as a child and treated me in that vein—doing his duty by me, to be sure, but taking only lightly the first thing of deep and serious import that had come into my life.

Chapter Four

THE RIVER WAS THE FASTEST MEANS of travel, and the most pleasant, as far as I was concerned. But that meant immediate separation from Karan, who would be marching ten tedious miles a day along the Grand Trunk Road, and would oversee the eventual removal of cumbersome luggage and luxuries, which were believed to be essential for the stay in Simla. So I resigned myself to life on the Ganges, weeks of living on a thatch-roofed houseboat. But at least it was an *ooluk,* the type of boat built more for speed than for safety. We were to go the first leg of the journey in this manner, then switch to a *puttaila,* shallow and flat bottomed, but safe in all kinds of weather. Returning home would be a dream, but heading up the sacred river was a tedious job. At times the boat had to be dragged along by a line of men, much as canal barges are towed. These poor creatures were forced to rise at daybreak, loosen the old boat's moorings, and start it off. If lucky, it would float down with the current. In some cases, the men were forced to walk upstream in water knee-deep, even waist-deep, dragging the vessel at a dismal mile an hour.

So the days dragged by slowly, all the more so due to the absence of Hugh and Arthur. Life on the river, with those two on board, had at least been an adventure. Seen through their eyes, all things took on an aura, from the trees, low and trailing in the water, to the *kunkur* cliffs, towering perpendicular rocks that lined one side of the river like a glowering barrier—not as much shutting the world out, but closing us in. Constance remained entirely confined to her room, with Rosina to hover over her and see to her needs to her heart's content. Thus I was granted the latitude of occasional freedom, and time up on deck.

The holy river is never still for a moment, and its banks are besieged with all sorts of human pilgrims, opportunists—as well as the pathetic dross and flotsam of humanity beguiled onto its shores. I was appalled at the number of beggars, famine-stricken peasants, who had left their own villages and come here to die. Their wasted bodies would be allowed to remain by the water until it rose, with the deluges of rain which the monsoon brought. Then their bones would be carried away by the blessed stream, all life returning unto the Mother River—and their souls would be ensured the blessing of reincarnation again.

Had it always been thus? Or on other like journeys had I been too preoccupied with the boys, indeed, with my own concerns to take notice? What was different now? I knew the answer, and I knew it lay inward. Something stirred within my own soul. Yet I was still wary of it, unwilling to face whatever it was I might discover there.

When I was working, all thoughts were pushed out of my conscious mind; and there was work in plenty to do. Constance may be picky, and at times broody, but she was suffering; I felt certain of that. Dr. Fielding had confided in me before we left that he feared her heart was not strong.

"She complains of nervous palpitations," he had said, "and her heartbeat is decidedly above normal. Dizziness and weakness—these are other symptoms she has suffered. This, as well as the high pressure of her blood, will be aggravated by stress—even the least amount."

He had raised his sandy brows and fixed me with a severe expression.

"You ask much, doctor," I said.

The corners of his mouth lifted slightly. "I know. Yes, I know that I do."

So we had talked, and determined all the precautions I must take with her. But both of us knew that all would be pointless, almost without value, unless Constance allowed our assistance to allay her own fears, to ease and soothe her—unless she allowed herself *hope*. For some reason she was holding the whole experience, holding this coming child at bay. For *the reason*—which must go forever unspoken and, like childish spooks and night spectres, grow in dread and power, just out of our reach.

At length we arrived in Cawnpore, over halfway to our destination. But the tedium of the river was near to driving us mad. Nights were the worst, at least for me. The restless longing I had begun to experience in Barrackpore assailed me again and again. Each evening when the vessel was moored the Hindu boatmen and servants would repair to the shore to prepare their one hot meal of the day, for Hindus refuse to cook food over water, only on good solid ground. The smells would waft up to me where I paced the cramped deck, the pungent food smells, and the swell and murmur of companionable speech. My loneliness at such times was terrible. I would then attempt to read, to answer correspondence, but my mind would not serve me, and my senses would not be still.

After the meal ended they would wash their brass utensils carefully and put out some *chupattees,* a form of unleavened bread, for eating the next day on board. I could hear the sounds; I knew what they were about. As the night settled into silence I could picture them in my mind's eye, stretched out on boards to sleep, with only a single *razai* for covering. But I knew they slept well. I knew they would arise with the dawn and be rested, and fit for another day.

To the banks of the beloved Ganges, in one form or another, all India comes. As we traveled the length of her, I found myself searching, watching the arch of a back, the tilt of a head—looking into faces for a glimpse of my mother.

Of course, not literally. But I knew what the English choose to forget, or to ignore altogether: the various tribes and peoples of India are in many cases as different from one another as Englishmen are from them. Hindu and Muslim alone mark a gulf that in most cases cannot be bridged. Such differences made the questions burn even stronger. What was my mother? What tribe did she hail from? What land had been hers? Was I even now passing the quiet mud and straw village where she had lived as a child?

Whenever I had asked questions of the major, during all my growing up years, he had always been vague and general, giving me the same tidbits of information, and no more, year after year. I did not ask Constance, not after the first attempt or two. Even with Vijaya, my ayah, the pattern had been much the same. But Vijaya had come with me, from my father's household. And if anyone knew . . .

I sought her out now, in the heat of the day, with the river a languid pool the boat squatted in. We left the other servants to their duties, and Constance to the dizziness the motion of the vessel caused in her. As soon as we two were alone, I asked her outright. "Tell me of my mother," I demanded.

At first she did not reply. I did not expect her to. I had been long accustomed to her slow, deliberate manner. But there was more than that here. She lowered her eyes and I noticed how many gray threads had woven themselves into her black hair. *How old is Vijaya?* I wondered, for perhaps the first time. She folded her thin brown hands into stillness. The *sari* she wore was a soft blue in color, yards and yards of soft cotton fabric wrapped around her lean frame, softening the contours, lending her a dignity that was lacking in our cumbersome English dresses.

"I know so little," she said. And her voice held the sadness of apology. "Much less than you will desire."

She was preparing me, at least in part, for disappointment. I swallowed against a dry, acid taste in my throat, and bade her go on.

"Your mother came from nowhere to your father's household. He took her in. He sheltered her, cared for her."

She was giving me the same old nonsense. But it led to one of my questions. "Why did she need sheltering? Was she in some sort of danger? Had she done something bad?"

The slightest alteration in Vijaya's expression alerted me; if I had not known her so well, I would have missed it. "She came from somewhere! Tell me!"

"She came from somewhere, yes. But that does not tell who she was." Vijaya sighed, trying to resign herself. "Your mother had been living among the 'Crims'."

I caught my breath, and she paused, allowing her words to sink in. I tried to laugh. "Is that why I, too, am fascinated by the Crow, by his eerie, almost mystical voice?"

There are fourteen million people in India who worship the Crow, whose dearest desire it is to return in their next incarnation in the form of this bird. Fourteen million people—every one a criminal, a legitimate criminal by point of his caste. It is, in fact, an honorable caste and calling in their eyes. They snatch money belts, pick pockets, remove expensive bangles from the ears of rich Indian dowagers. They also rob travelers and unsuspecting houses, which they have previously studied, learning the characteristics and the habits of the household with care. They do not mind the danger; the danger is an added spice to them, for they sincerely believe that the surest way of gaining paradise is to die while engaged in their sacred calling of committing a crime.

"My mother came as a gypsy then?" I remember that the boat seemed to rock, almost shiver beneath us, and my head felt light as I asked the question.

"She was only a child, younger than you are."

"Were you there?"

Vijaya shook her head. "I was brought in to be your ayah when you were born."

"But—" I sensed there was more.

"My husband worked in Captain Simmons household."

"So you did see my mother when first she came?"

Her silence confirmed it.

"She was a Crim spy, selling fruit, selling baskets, getting information to be used in robbing the place." I knew the entire Crim intelligence network was composed of its women, whom they considered to be more intelligent, more clever than men. I knew the gypsy spies played on the weaknesses about them—silly women and fickle men, who would say things that they shouldn't, in unguarded moments.

"She was very young," Vijaya repeated. "And needless to say, your father's house was not robbed."

"Why did she stay? Why did she marry my father?"

For the first Vijaya smiled. "Your father was a very charming man. Handsome to look at. And kind."

"And he took pity on her?" I tried to recreate the two of them in my mind: her dark, vulnerable youth, his laughing mouth and red hair curling over his forehead.

"She was not a Crow. She was not of their kind. She had come to them"—she hesitated—"some other way."

"What way?"

Vijaya shook her head. "I do not know that. Truly, missysahib, I don't."

I walked away from her and leaned over the rail of the low boat and tried to think. I knew it had been common, even accepted practice in my father's time for officers to take Indian wives—*bubus,* they called them. Indeed, the company provided a small subsidy to encourage a man to do so. They believed it engendered stability, and it probably did. The practice had disintegrated into disuse, and what had grown customary today was the taking of common courtesans as "temporary wives." These women, after all, were highly skilled in those areas which brought pleasure to men. Were wives so very different, be they Indian or British? I wished I knew. *Certain practices permissible, understood, winked at,* I thought. *And yet,* something within me protested, *I am forbidden to form any sort of an attachment to an Indian man.*

I dismissed my ayah and watched her glide away from me. I was aware of the heat, oppressive as a blanket pressing against the pores of my skin. I was aware of the dull slap of the water against the boat, the sounds of water buffalo, lumbering and complaining, at the water's edge. With a keen, yet dazed awareness I heard everything, and yet nothing at all. Some vital inner part of me had gone far away, seeking through thick mists of darkness for sights that were not its to see. The only face that came to me was the face of Karan, and his brown eyes were sad. And their gaze held a certain remonstrance that pierced my heart.

We reached Gurmuktesar, and the river curved north toward Mussoorie and Landour. We disembarked for a short overland journey by palkee dak, which would bring us to the hills and our destination at last.

Constance was a good sport, I must say, though the *kahars*, or bearers, lifted her up with a groan, saying, *"Bhuya, burra bhair,"* or, "Brother, it is very heavy."

But they trotted on for their allotted ten miles until a change of bearers, and in this manner we made our way to Simla. And what a grand sight awaited us there! Snow-capped mountains crowned the distant landscape, with such a suggestion of coolness that my spirits at once lifted. All about us was green and blooming and fragrant. That was the difference—there was *air* here, air to breathe deep into the lungs, air that felt clean, that carried the taste of the far mountains and the thin, cold sky.

The servants set about airing the rooms, removing the protective dust sheets from the teakwood furniture, unloading boxes and seeing about fixing the memsahib something to eat. With Rosina's help I got Constance to lie down and allow us to bathe her hot, dusty skin with a sponge dipped into a basin of cool water. As she gave way to our ministrations, I could feel her relax. She let her eyelids close as though they had suddenly grown too heavy.

"There will be peace for weeks," I promised her, "with absolutely nothing to do. Rosina will fan you, and I shall read you stories—clever stories that make you laugh. Gopal is the best cook here, but we will keep his skills a secret, and he will labor only for you. Spinach with eggs and tapioca soup, your favorites. And, of course, coconut cake and mango brulee." Thus did I beguile her, and tease her away from herself.

She sighed. A light smile lifted the corners of her mouth, which was so often narrowed these last months in discomfort or pain. "If the boys were here, they would spoil it all, wouldn't they, with their pranks and loud games."

Then I knew, really knew for the first time, that she missed her sons with a fierce loneliness which I could not even imagine. I put the sponge to her forehead and kissed the dry white skin of her cheek.

Simla is a huddle of very ordinary bungalows clinging precariously to a series of steep slopes that rise seven thousand feet above the sea. That is one way in which to look at it. It is also a city built by the British gods for their pleasure. Close at hand lie the wonders of temples, mosques, and half-buried ruins, all of ancient and exotic origin. But the English occupied themselves on the cricket and polo fields, the racetrack and the croquet green, the garden picnics and the evening dinner affairs. The art of India, the weird gods and strange deities, were as nothing to them. Well, not quite nothing, I must admit if I am to be fair. They were considered curiosities to be described in the letters sent back home, and to be sketched on lazy afternoons, as a sort of proof that one had really been to such places. It was all the rage for English ladies, and sometimes gentlemen as well, to try their hand at sketching. Even I was guilty of such presumption upon a few occasions, along with the rest.

We settled in. A routine established itself that was much diminished from our usual times here. But I was not a servant, I had little to keep me occupied. There were a few other girls of my age in families, or as survivals of the fishing fleet who had ended up among us. The only trouble was that they were generally not of my kind. I committed to only the minimal engagements for picnics in the rose gardens of the Viceregal Lodge, walks along shaded wooded paths, and sets of croquet.

Constance served as a splendid excuse for me at such times when I wanted my privacy above the petty amusements which came to bore me so quickly. I may have allowed myself to become almost dangerously retiring if it were not for one thing: I had not as yet caught sight of Karan nor figured out where he might be.

I knew he was attached to the Nineteenth Regiment, whose four squadrons included Punjabi, Muslims, Dogras, Pathans, and Sikhs such as himself. I knew he had duties and responsibilities to see to; I feared the dread possibility of never meeting him here in this mountain fastness at all.

Then one afternoon, a good fortnight following our arrival, I was seated under the shade of a spreading guava tree in the leafy, fragrant solitude of the herbaceous border lining the viceroy's lodge, and I sensed his presence. Without looking up, I could feel him. The short hairs on my arm seemed to stand on end. I held my breath, not wanting to move, scarcely daring to hope.

"Charlotte." He spoke my name as no other spoke it, seeming to curl his tongue around the syllables in a kind of caress. "*Namaste,*" he murmured. I lifted my gaze as he folded his palms together and his body curved toward me in gracious acknowledgment. With a shiver of anticipation, I met his eyes. An Englishman's eyes can dance with delight or burn with passion, but they cannot pulse with the warmth of the Indian. I thought I would melt in that warmth.

"To my people white is the color of sadness and mourning. Yet you Englishwomen always wear white."

He had spoken in an effort to lighten the tension that was laced between us so thickly, but his words displeased me somehow. *You Englishwomen*—did he mean anything by that? Was he attempting to state his views, remind me of my place, remind me of the gulf that separated us?

"I have been in a sort of mourning these past weeks," I answered.

He shook his head ever so slightly, but no more. For he saw in my eyes that I meant more than he knew.

"I am not an Englishwoman, as you yourself have reminded me." I struggled to keep the sharp pique I was feeling from sounding like a girlish petulance in my voice. "I am confused and lonely, so lonely deep inside myself. I *am* becoming a woman, and for the first time I want to know of that woman whose lot it was to bear me and then to disappear from my life. I want to know who she was, and who I am because of her!"

With an effort that was visible he kept his distance. His hands sat like stones at his sides. "Does no one know? Is there no one to tell you?"

"On the ship I questioned Vijaya, my ayah, who has been with me from the beginning." I paused, wondering how to condense, how to express the things she had told me.

He inclined his body and squinted his eyes at me. "She had too little to tell you, and you did not like what she said."

"Can you read me so easily?" I spoke the question sharply; he dropped his eyes in humble apology. "Do not play the native with me!" I snapped. I did not like the obsequious manner the Indians adopted with the British lords, especially when it was Karan. "It is not like that between you and me."

"Isn't it?" His voice, too, had a bite to it. I had not offended him, but I had hurt him, which was a far worse offense.

"Yes, yes, you settled that matter before we left Barrackpore." I waved his brooding aside. "But we are not in agreement on that, as we are on many other things." I smiled, hoping what beauty he might see in me would work for me now. "Do you agree, my young lord, that God has blessed us with a most lovely afternoon, which is swiftly slipping away?"

His mouth lifted despite himself.

"And might you agree that a walk through the viceroy's gardens would prove a singular pleasure on such a day?"

He was finding it difficult to resist me. "I might."

I moved and, before he could stop me, linked my arm into his, the white of my thin lawn dress standing in stark contrast to the solid blue of his sleeve. "Shall we?" I took a step forward, and he followed suit. He was humoring me; I knew he was humoring me. He was deeply distressed, and I was not playing fair. But he understood that, he understood why, and forgave me. He, too, was in pain, and therefore would not judge the way the pain assailed me, nor my inability to hold it at bay.

Chapter Five

Karan and I met often. It was so easy to manage, and therefore so difficult to resist. I was a person of no consequence, really, and he of less. Neither Constance nor Major Reid were on hand to observe and protest. We were careful, we held to the rules of propriety; we did not fall into unseemly ways. But I knew what it was my heart wanted, and I sincerely believed that I could find a way to achieve my desires.

He did not kiss me again. Indeed, he was careful to avoid the slightest physical contact. And though I knew why, I could not bear to be near him and yet denied even the slightest comfort of his arm around my shoulder or his hand over mine.

Early in August we had a spell of unseasonably cold, wet weather, when even the close peaks and rock sides were shrouded in mist. Mist choked the small hollows and ravines, distorting the landscape so that even those of us most familiar with our surroundings walked out with care.

Major Reid was expected any day. Later, Constance claimed that she had believed that she heard him calling to her, and she had run out of the bungalow to go to him without further thought. Why she remained when he failed to make an appearance and why she strayed from the path—these were questions that would never find answers. In her confusion, disoriented by the dense mist, she stumbled and fell.

Rosina found her. She could not move her alone, and after

crying for help and receiving no answer at all, she ran to find Dr. Fielding, who, as the kind fates would have it, was enjoying a drink with some of his comrades. Of course, he went with her at once. They lifted Constance and carried her back to her bed, and made sure she was warm, with blankets and hot packs, and a hot herbal tea coaxed down her throat. She wouldn't stop shivering. The doctor feared pneumonia; he feared a strain on her heart. She was beginning to show signs of toxemia, which can be deadly in import. And Major Reid did not come. I stayed by her side for nearly twenty hours, dozing into a black numbness, when I could not prevent it, that was nothing like sleep. Only once she cried out, but it was neither for me nor Rosina, nor for the major himself. She cried out for Roselyn. I bent close and whispered soothingly to her, but a chill crept up my spine.

I thought it a bad omen. But of course I told no one, and only prayed all the harder. Even at the times she was conscious she did not seem to recognize me. No one spoke of her condition, nor of the child, nor of anything that would serve to disturb her at all. After the first day she began having periodic contractions. The third day they became regular and closer together, yet she still seemed unaware of what was happening.

Later that night when the doctor had sent us all out of the room, save the two nurses he had brought with him, the baby was born—feet first, so it was a breech birth and difficult, and she lost too much blood. But when the doctor walked out of the room, sagging with weariness, and looked at me, I knew that she was all right.

"The child?" I had mouthed the words more than I had spoken them.

An expression entered Alan Fielding's eyes that sent a thrill of fear through me. But then he smiled. "A girl. A perfect little girl, and I believe that she will make it just fine."

The nurses stayed. There were plenty to see to the needs of the child and the mother. I walked out into the dark. Cool air poured down from a mighty rift in the mountain above me. I could smell the wet trees and the crushed green of the dense upland foliage. I closed my eyes, threw my head back, and drank in the restoring scents. When I opened my eyes again, Karan was standing before me. He did not say a word. He held out his arms, and I found myself cradled against the pleasurable warmth of him. There were tears in my eyes. I blinked them back, but they kept coming to shame me.

"Is Constance all right?" The question was a murmur spoken with his lips on my hair.

I moved my head and tried to speak, but the words would not come. He stroked my hair with the length of his long, lean fingers, and the touch soothed me. But I could feel a tension in his body that tingled along my own skin.

Then he lifted my face and put a finger against my lips. "Dear one, do not try to speak." He bent his head and kissed the tears on my cheeks. I cried out then, and he kissed my mouth with a trembling tenderness. I remember thinking that this was what life was meant for, that all the stumbling and searching, the pain and cruelty—even the ordinary caprices of living—were meant to contrast and enhance such moments that brought our spirits near enough to heaven to make all the suffering worthwhile, even sanctified.

Constance called the child Lucinda Jane, after both her own grandmothers. But from the beginning, we all called her Lucy. The first few days Constance did little more than sleep the sleep of exhaustion while her body mended. Lucy displayed the undemanding temperament of an angel from the very start. We of the household stumbled over one another in our efforts to care for her, and she seemed to appreciate all we did, though she was but a newly born infant. I swear that she smiled whenever anyone fed her, changed her nappies, or rocked her gently, enjoying the delicate scent and feel of her. She had brought a spirit of contentment into the house.

Then one morning Constance awoke, sat bolt upright, and began barking orders again. She was her old self, or so it appeared. But something was different. Although she demanded absolute control, as was her way, she seemed always tense and distracted. And behind her eyes lurked a fear that bordered on panic. She said nothing, but it was apparent at once that the focus of her obsession was Lucy; she would not let the child out of her sight. Those of us who understood best the cause of this behavior were the most patient with her. But she wore us all out—as well as confining us to the horrors of her sickroom, for her demands were precise and literal: the infant must be constantly by her side. Even when Rosina talked Constance into bathing herself in the luxury of warm, perfumed waters, a nurse had to sit in the same room with the child on her lap. It grew more than tedious; it created an atmosphere of madness that permeated the house. Then, as though he had been dropped down from heaven, the major came home.

For a few hours the joy of his arrival crowded out everything else. Even Constance rallied; two spots of pale pink, like the beginning blush on new fruit, colored her cheeks. She was proud of the baby, overjoyed by the expression on her husband's face whenever he gazed down at his daughter. She had accomplished the impossible, and both she and the child had lived through it. And Lucinda Jane was beautiful, with tiny, well-formed ears peeking from under thick curls of black hair, a delicate nose, a well-shaped mouth, and fair, silky skin. A dream child, too good to be true. I wondered if that was what Constance was thinking.

The sense of bliss, so welcome, was short-lived. Several hours after the major's arrival he had coaxed Constance out into the garden with him. It was small as English gardens go, but well laid out, and shaded. And as evening softened the contours of tree and rock and drew out the scents of the flowers, it was almost a magical place. He drew her arm through his and patted her hand with affection. I was only a few steps behind, and I watched her back stiffen, her head go straight, and her hand, where he held it, tremble. She whirled on me, and her eyes blazed so coldly that I shrank back.

"Where is Lucy?" She screamed the words. I stood, startled.

"You did not ask me to bring her. The evening air has turned a bit. She is safe in Radha's care."

"Deceptive, disobedient girl! You know what is expected of you!" Her hand rose up and then struck my cheek, with the speed and strength of a serpent. I gasped and put my hand to the sting. The major looked at Constance as though he was not sure that he knew her.

"Just what is expected of the child?" he asked. His voice was deceptively low and calm. From experience we both knew this tone and respected it.

But Constance was far gone. She worked to control herself; the struggle was visible. "All members of the household have been told that Lucinda is to be *with me!*" She spoke the last words through clenched teeth; that fear which spoke of panic began to tremble in her eyes.

"With you, yes. But surely not every moment. The child is being cared for now, by a capable nurse and ayah."

"No!" The one word was a cry of anguish more than anything else. I stepped back off the path. The major put his arm around Constance's shoulder and led her back to the house. All the servants made way for them. The silence was so loud that I wanted to put my hands to my ears.

He led her into her room. Radha brought the baby and laid the wide-eyed infant in her mother's arms. The major ordered a hot drink laced with one of the sedatives Dr. Fielding had ordered. The household began to draw breath and relax again. I went to my own room and tried to concentrate on one of my favorite books of poetry. Constance had never struck me before, at least not in that manner, and not for a very long time. There were stinging swats against my backside when I was a child and she lost patience with me. But this—

Unable to concentrate on the words before me, I waited uneasily for the summons I knew would come.

The servants had been sent out. I stood alone with Major Reid in the small front parlor of the bungalow. No lamp had been lit. The dim coolness seemed appropriate.

"Lottie, my dear."

I tried to smile at him. I hated the misery I saw in his eyes. "Do not be concerned, sir. She didn't mean—Constance is not herself lately."

His gaze darkened. "That is no excuse for her behavior."

"Yes, it is," I argued. "She is terrified, Major. Have you seen—in her eyes . . ."

He nodded miserably. "But why, Lottie? Why?" His anguish and confusion reached out to me. Nothing is quite so pitiful as seeing a strong, capable man, wise and well fitted for the work of life, rendered helpless and distraught by forces he cannot control and does not understand. I placed my hand on his arm.

"'Tis a pity you've had to find her like this, sir; come all this way—"

"What is it, Lottie? What do you think has caused it?"

I shook my head. "I've been agonizing over that question these last weeks, believe me." I ran my hand through my hair. "I could reason out part of it, perhaps." I drew a deep breath. He was watching me so closely that his gaze threatened to suffocate me. "All along Constance has wanted this child to be a daughter to make up for the loss of Roselyn." I spoke the words gently, but he sighed at the sound of his dead daughter's name.

"Both you and I knew that," I reminded him. "And we knew how dangerously deep that desire went, for she could not bear to speak of it, to voice the hope of it aloud. Now that Lucy is here—and at a price we cannot imagine—and more perfect, I suppose, than Constance even dared hope for—"

"Yes, yes." The major spoke the words slowly and thoughtfully. I had set him to thinking. "Something snapped in her then."

"But what made it snap?" I took up his line of thinking. "I am come to believe that the joy of possession—of having her fondest hopes realized—is too painful to bear."

The major's head shot up; he was listening carefully. "The joy is too precious to bear losing! And the risk of loss is inherent in every breath that she takes."

He did not reply for a moment. I could almost hear his mind working. "So you would say her only defense—as she sees it—is to beat Life at its own game, to hold all dangers at bay—"

"By dint of her own overwhelming desire!" Just speaking the words out loud exhausted me. "Oh, Major Reid," I breathed, "think how tormented the poor thing must be."

The room had grown very dark. I could no longer see the expressions that played over his face. He shuffled, in his usual awkward gait, closer. "God bless you, you're a treasure, Lottie. What would we do without you?"

He leaned forward and planted a kiss on my forehead. His affection both warmed and strengthened me, and I wondered if he realized that it had always been himself who had spoken with kindness or praise to me, never Constance, and yet he always spoke in the plural: "You have made *us* proud"; "What would *we* do without you?" The irony was, of course, that Constance could not do without me. I wondered, too, as I lit a candle and made my way to my room, if his words had been in part an apology—an acknowledgment of that very thing?

The major possessed powers altogether lacking in the rest of us. He coaxed Constance to sit in the cool garden with him of an evening, and to spend her mornings sewing in the sunny parlor that fronted the house. Of course, Lucy was always with her—that was to be understood. But soon her friends began coming, one by one, to pay their respects and to feast their eyes on the baby—a rare and delightful sight among women of her age. Some of them laughed outright when they saw her sitting in state with a newborn infant, but they laughed with surprised pleasure, and I believe Constance understood. None were so boorish to suggest that she looked more the part of the grandmother, and what was she doing at her age? They had more manners than that and, I'd like to think, more real feeling. And Lucy *was* terribly beautiful for a child so young and so small. It was natural that Constance should be proud of her, but it was the fierceness of her pride, like the fierceness of all else about her, that was painful to see. The scene that occurred in the garden the night of the major's arrival was never mentioned between us. I had not thought it would be. Constance had never been one to demean herself by forthright apology. And yet it stood, just like a small, cold shadow between us. Perhaps Constance could ignore it, but I was not able to pretend it away.

As Constance grew stronger and the household adapted to the altered schedule necessitated by his arrival, the major spent less and less time at home. That was to be expected. He was an officer, here among his fellow officers, and for only a few weeks at that. He was a great enthusiast of polo, and had as much a weakness for horse racing as any of the gentlemen here. He spent a great deal of time at the track; I have no idea how much money. The bright life of Simla went on around us, but the major alone was a part of it. I considered it a bit dull, in view of both my own preferences and my circumstances. The days wore their languid way toward the inevitable. One morning the major announced that we would leave the mountains in eight days and begin our long journey home.

I remember two things about the last week in Simla. One was the night of the dance—an occasion so like the dozens of others I had attended in the scant time since I, a seventeen-year-old, had been admitted to society, that I wondered how these women, especially those who had been wives in India for ten years or more, could avoid being bored to distraction! Most of the men—as is well known among us—were past any age which could even politely be referred to as "young." Those out here fishing for husbands understood this, and were quite happily reconciled to catching a mature man with a decent income and an admirable pension; indeed, they usually deemed themselves fortunate if such was their lot.

But I stayed and did what was expected of me, and hid my true feelings with my usual skill. It is odd I should remember dancing with Major Hillard, but I do. He was a man not many years younger than my father would have been, with thin brown hair that had been faded by the Indian sun so that it appeared to have the mottled shades of moss and that moss-like quality of looking both springy and crushed. He had a full mouth, partially concealed by the long mustache he wore. That much I remember. And I remember how firm his hands were on my arm and my waist. He spoke of his wife, Judith, who I knew—as all the camp did—was a pretty thing much younger than himself. She was ailing; she had been ailing for months now. Dr. Fielding feared consumption and believed she should be sent home—but she was not yet strong enough to survive the ardors of the journey. Inexplicably, I remember thinking: *I feel sorry for her, but not for him. There is something too pat, too formulaic about the way he discusses her. I do not see any pain in his eyes.*

Who was I to judge, of course? Many people—I believe myself included—are masters at concealing their feelings, at putting on a brave face for others, of bearing their sorrows in a silence of mingled faith and pride. But I was to remember that initial reaction many times in the future.

There was much to be done in the way of packing, organizing supplies, putting the gardens to sleep, and settling the house for our absence. But then, we had many servants. Even with the major in company I found time to spend one last evening with Karan.

In India there is no twilight. Darkness comes, and one's only awareness is that the darkness grows richer, deeper in essence. With darkness comes the magic of fireflies, legions of fairy lamps that pierce the low expanse of the black sky and light the fields, choking the hollows and roadsides with a thick, eerie glow. They meant childhood to me, and all the pure joy that attends it. And perhaps for that reason, I felt Roselyn near to me as I walked out that night.

Karan came toward me looking more tall and regal than usual, the white of his turban almost glowing against the ebony backdrop of the night sky, his face framed by it in warm relief, his eyes seeming to glow from under his turban like the small, enchanted insects.

He reached for my hand. "Charlotte, Charlotte . . ." The speaking of my name—he need do no more to enchant me.

"We are to be parted again." In the shadows I could not read his expression, but his next words startled me.

"You must know—and never forget—that if we were to be parted this very night, not to meet for years, or perhaps never to meet in this life again . . ."

I could feel myself holding my breath. Why was he saying this?

"I would still love you—with the same intensity, the same joy and devotion that flows through me right now."

I could not answer him. At last, when my trembling eased some, I demanded in a whisper, "Why do you say such strange things? Are you attempting to frighten me?" I could hear the pain rising to panic in my voice, but I didn't care. "Are you trying to wrench my heart from out of me?"

"*Bas, bas!*" he murmured, meaning, "Hush, hush." "Forgive me, Charlotte. I meant only to reassure you, to calm your heart!" He wound his fingers through the tendrils of my hair. "Life is so uncertain . . . and you are so dear to me! I wished you to have heard these words—I wish you to fasten them for all time in your heart!"

He pressed his cool lips against my cheek. "Perhaps you shall hear them time and time again, my dear one. But let you hear them first now."

I leaned against him, suddenly more for support than for the pleasure of feeling the touch of him. He let me stand there, until the trembling ceased altogether. Then we moved, hand in hand, along a cool, shadowed path that rose above the houses until all marks of civilized man fell away. We were as two spirits communing together, with no barriers between us. A scattering of fireflies pulsed about our feet. Often we walked in silence, for there was much between us that did not need to be said.

I took the sweetness of those last hours with me, like a blessing, like a talisman that nothing pale and ordinary—nothing cruel or deceitful—had the power to dim.

Chapter Six

The return journey was of a different nature altogether—less tedious, yet nerve-racking in the extreme. True, we had the major's strength, direction, and authority to sustain us; indeed, without him I do not believe we'd have made it. Radha may have deserted, slipped into the shadows at one of our moorings, never appearing again. And I may have been rendered unstable and gone off into fits, like one of the dervishes whose sacred dances work men to the point of wild fury which could drive a soul mad.

The short distance we traveled by palkee went reasonably well, for Constance could stretch inside the long, boxlike enclosure nearly full-length on rugs and pillows, with the baby nestled beside her. And when we stopped each night at the dak bungalows along the roadway, the major was there to order hot baths and secure *moorgee,* or curried fowl, that was edible.

Going down river toward Calcutta, traveling with the current, meant we could cover a distance of some eight hundred miles, as the crows flies, in six to eight weeks. The season of monsoon winds and drenching rains was officially over, but Mother Nature, for some reason of her own, was sloppy, and our first two days on the river were gray and dismal, with a colorless sky running like watered ink into the colorless river, and the constant drizzle of a cold, wet rain. We shivered, huddling together for companionship as much as for warmth. And

Constance, rather than fussing in concern and frustration, grew distant and cold, and perhaps even more demanding than a distraught Constance would have been.

No one could do anything right, not in the least; and they heard about it in curt, biting terms. Her disdain embraced every one of us, even the major. And, of course, the effect upon him was to cause him to distance himself from her as much as possible. We of her household, however, did not share that luxury. Her disapproval was constant and stinging; our tempers grew short from the effects of it. Even our faces showed the strain and the weariness.

Here, not being a servant proper, I had some means of escape. And though I felt guilty, I was prone to avail myself of it whenever I could. But other than escape from Constance, there was little for me to do, little to help the time pass. The life of the river moved around us, but we were not part of it. The pressing humanity, the smells of poverty, the listless, accepting gaze of the many eyes that looked back at me, enraged me. The injustices of life—the *waste*—assailed my senses and wounded my spirit. Karan had made this possible. Because I had been ready to see, his had been the power to open my eyes, my inner sight. Such sight was so painful, and carried a demand all its own.

One afternoon of slow progress along a dull stretch skirting the sandbars, I noticed a commotion at the river's edge. Three tall elephants—magnificent creatures—their backs padded with thick oriental rugs, and their faces decorated in an intricate pattern of bright colors, were approaching the water's edge. Each carried three men on his back, three men of high caste and importance; one could tell that at a glance. I admire elephants, so I positioned myself at the railing to enjoy the sight of them. As I watched, two small beggar lads raced toward the beasts in a game of sport, racing with childish abandon. The foremost boy, glancing over his shoulder to check the progress of his companion, looked up too late to see the broad gray side of the elephant only inches away from him. In sudden panic he tried to check his speed, but his bare feet slid in the thick mud, and in an instant he was under the large beast's feet. The elephant was frightened, and his rider, angry at the disturbance, pulled him up short, upsetting the balance of the big feet, so that one of them landed squarely on the fallen boy's head. A scream pierced the air; before it was ended, a score—ten score voices joined it. The parents and the people of the crushed boy pressed forward. The three elephants were goaded to turn *into* the crowd. I diverted my gaze, a sick feeling beginning to gnaw at me, when I heard a voice at my elbow.

"Look at those fools. For the sake of one thoughtless beggar lad they would see half their children trampled."

It was a woman's voice that had spoken these callous words. I raised my eyes slowly to meet her disinterested gaze. "Quite a show, don't you think?" she remarked. "Aren't they wonderful beasts, especially that one in the rear with the turquoise drawings all down his nose?"

I was staring openmouthed, so that the woman had no choice but to check herself. "Really, my dear," she said, distaste at my lack of manners thick in her voice. "Get hold of yourself. Such things happen every day; they are a part of life here, and certainly none of our concern."

She turned and walked away from me. I leaned against the rail, trembling with emotions far stronger than her cold disdain.

Though my skin is not sallow-white, I thought, as if from a distance, *but a warm honey brown, she took me for an Englishwoman—one of the privileged, the conquering class.*

I wasn't being fair; I knew I wasn't. The natives of India butchered and tortured one another with cruel and practiced disregard; they were no better than the English. What *was* the matter with me? What tender or simply timid strain of either my mother's or my father's did I carry? I stood with my hands clenching the rail while the boat moved away from the scene on the shore, and I collected my wits about me again.

We were too weary when we reached Barrackpore to do much more than stumble gratefully into the bungalow in search of our beds. That the servants' hands were busy while we rested was nothing short of a miracle to me. I awoke after hours of a drugged, dreamless sleep to the smell of lamb and Gopal's hot curry, and I lay with my eyes closed, just savoring the awareness of home.

That first meal, which should have been a relaxed affair with the sweetness of homecoming in it, was awkward and strained. Lucy, exhausted and a bit out of sorts from the journey, fussed in her mother's arms, then in the small woven cradle at Constance's feet. Her cry became more than annoying; it grated on our every nerve; yet Constance could not get her to stop.

"Let me take Lucy Jane from here, bathe her in cool water, and prepare her for bed." Radha stood humbly at her mistress's elbow, speaking in the same soothing voice she might have used with a child.

Constance fixed her with a withering look which said, *How dare you!* But she did not deign to answer vocally so lowly a request.

Radha made the dread mistake of persisting in her gracious request which, in itself—as Constance viewed things—was insupportable cruelty.

The mistress banged her fist on the table. "Leave this room!" she shouted at the ayah. "And leave this house. I will not brook such insolent insubordination!"

Radha stood blinking for a moment, then bowed herself out. The silence was heavy. The major pushed his chair back with a loud scrape and left the table. I toyed with the food that remained on my plate, then excused myself, too. Lucy was still screaming and Constance sitting stiff and unmoving at her place when I walked out of the room.

I avoided Constance for the remainder of the evening; I did not trust myself to speak to her without some kind of remonstrance. Thus I was surprised to look up and see her enter my room—cradling a now-sleeping Lucy in her arms.

"Do you think it unjust, what I did at the table?"

Her question took me completely off guard. I kept my eyes on the bed as I attempted to answer. "Yes, I do. And unwise as well." It was the coward in me that made me divert her attention, even slightly, from the issue.

"Radha is an excellent ayah," I continued. "You had not a complaint; indeed, you praised her highly when she had care of the boys." I longed to add: *She was good enough for them, but she is not good enough for this hallowed daughter.* Instead I said, "She is both good and wise. You must trust her, Constance. You will wear yourself out."

I could feel her set her mind against what I was saying. "Well, you shall have your way of it. Ralph went over my head and spoke to Radha himself—increasing her wages, if you can believe it, to compensate for the injury!"

Her voice was so cold that it stunned me. "Good," I replied, very matter-of-factly. "We could not manage without her, and I doubt we could find anyone half as trained or as trustful to replace her."

Constance said nothing, so I touched the baby's hand with my finger. "She really is lovely," I said. Her eyes smiled, but no muscle on her face moved. "And she is well formed and healthy, and—"

"You are wasting your effort, Lottie."

For the second time Constance took me off guard. "What do you mean?" I responded, deciding to force her to say the dread words aloud.

"No one understands—not even you. I should not have expected it." She seemed to draw herself up, and she was already imposing enough standing there, even with the sleeping child in her arms.

"You know nothing of what this child means to me, or of what a mother's responsibility is."

I opened my mouth to respond, but she stopped me with a gesture.

"You mock me. But when you have experienced pain like mine, then see how you behave."

I said nothing; I made no move. She took a step toward the

door and then paused. "Someday, Lottie, for all your pat answers, all your knowing, you will regret your cruelty to me."

I gasped; she must have heard me. She crossed to the door and shut it behind her very gently before making her way down the hall.

My birthday fell in late October. It fell into the vacuum of days such as I have described. Turning eighteen surely meant something special in a young woman's life. Constance presented me with gifts, but it was through duty she gave them, not pleasure. Yet her sense of duty, for some reason undoubtedly tied to her child, was suddenly irritating her conscience and her memory.

"I wonder," she mused as we sipped our late morning tea, "if I did wrong in not sending you and Roselyn to England when you were girls."

I choked on the bite I was chewing, thoroughly amazed by her question. We had never once spoken of this subject before.

"You know why you did it." Robust and full of life as she appeared, Roselyn's health had always been delicate. She suffered a serious bout of consumption at the age of seven. After that, Constance would not even talk about sending her away. Instead, we suffered a series of tutors—some quite horrid, one in particular gifted with children, who instilled within me my first desire to learn. When Roselyn died we were both thirteen, too old for me to think of beginning a formal education. And if Constance were to send me away, she would destroy the last reminder of Roselyn.

Constance was watching me. "Oh, yes," she said dryly. "Yet I lost her anyway, didn't I?"

I could not humor her, not the way I used to. "You did the best you could. At least she died in your arms, not in the sick-room of a cold, impersonal English school."

She gasped and put her hand to her throat. I don't believe I would have said what I did if not for Hugh and Arthur. Their last letters had not been able to disguise the barrenness, even harshness of their lives in England, despite their attempts to be manly and stoic, as their father would expect.

"I was thinking of the boys," I said, relenting a little.

"You do not understand, Lottie. You know only this one place, this one way of life."

I cannot believe the effrontery of the British! "Kindness is kindness, wherever you find it," I countered. "You may believe narrowness and cruelty build character; I do not."

"You think me wrong for defending a system you do not understand?"

I shrugged my shoulders and drew my napkin from my lap. My position in this household had been singular since Roselyn's death. I had never been quite a daughter, rather a foundling who was fortunate to be raised with her Roselyn. I was not mistreated, surely not by English standards. Thanks to the major in particular, I had even known my share of affection. But with Roselyn gone, I was not forced into the position of surrogate daughter; I was not required to try to take her place, to fill the void she had left. Rather, my own position seemed lowered a notch or two. I was not generally resented or punished for being the one who had lived while Roselyn died. But I *felt* it, especially from Constance. At times she could not contain the pain of her loss, the injustice of what was constantly present before her eyes: I lived and flourished—I, who was without parents or prospects—while Roselyn, who would have lived a favored and pampered life, had been taken away.

Even as a child I could understand what she was feeling, see the injustice from her point of view. It was simply that I was enduring my own form of suffering, and I desperately needed someone to see that—acknowledge it—and do something to help me through.

Life is not like that though, is it? It seldom answers our expectations nor caters to our needs. I had learned that, but I was not reconciled to the knowing—not then, not even now.

Barrackpore is not a large post. That, aided by the strict routine of things and the close-knit nature of each segment of the social strata, created a condition not conducive to young lovers, especially those who must meet in a clandestine manner. But it was my birthday; I intended to see Karan, whatever the consequences.

We met at the far end of the park in a little hollow behind a stand of palm and plantain, which would serve well to shield us from sight. The heavy trumpet creepers and the winding cypress vines twined in thick coils and swung freely in the breeze that was coming up from the river. The shadows of evening were already crawling in ever-lengthening patterns along the ground.

"*Namaste,*" I greeted him. But he did not return my salutation. He smiled and said instead, "I should like to see you with your hair smoothed back with coconut oil—pulled back tight the way our women wear it, with a little red *sindoor* powder right here, where your hair would part—" He touched the spot with his finger. "And a *kumkum* of red powder on your forehead." He pressed his lips to the place where the mark of beauty would be.

"Aye, and bangles." I took up the strain. "Anklets and arm bands and bracelets up to my elbows."

"And perhaps the smallest ring of gold and ivory to grace your beautiful nose."

We spoke in a light vein, but there was deep feeling behind the words he spoke.

"I will never dress that way," I replied. And as I spoke the words, I knew they were true. "I will never adorn myself as one of your fair ones. I will never be an Indian woman." I did not realize there were tears in my eyes.

"You will always be an Indian woman," he replied.

"You speak in paradoxes, and you toy with my feelings," I scolded.

"I do not mean to. I speak what I see as truth."

"I am neither Indian nor English."

"You are both," he insisted. "Have we not discussed this before?"

He drew me down to sit in the soft mosses beneath the

plantains. He drummed the soft ground with the tips of his long fingers. His eyes grew dark and serious.

"You have not been taught proper respect for your sex, for your station as a woman," he began. "One of the ancient beliefs of the Hindu nation is that the wife is the husband's spiritual helpmeet, his *saha-dharmini.* No married man performs a religious rite or ceremony without being joined in it by his wife. Otherwise, it would be considered faulty and incomplete. A man cannot live a full spiritual life unless he moves in harmony with his wife."

I was interested. But what I had observed of Hindu life did not reflect Karan's sayings. "This is the ideal," I said.

"This is the ideal," he agreed. "But I have lived in the quiet villages. I have seen such a life practiced by men and women, where you have not."

"Education is encouraged for high-class Hindu women," Karan continued. "Can you say as much of the British? In science as well as poetry, the writings of women are studied and held in the highest regard."

I thought of my mother; I could not help it. Had she been an educated woman? Probably not. What had her feelings been about life and the purpose of things?

"It is said by us that one mother is greater than a thousand fathers." Karan was watching me closely.

"Do you really believe it?"

"The Supreme Being of the Universe is to us the Divine Mother. We pray to her as the source of all wisdom and virtue. We believe her spirit dwells in every feminine form that graces the earth."

I sighed. The gathering darkness obscured his features and any expression that played there. How dear his face had become to me! How soothing and strengthening the mere sound of his voice!

"I have a gift for you," he said, drawing something out of his pocket. "It belonged to my mother."

I drew back. "Then it is too dear to be giving to me."

He laughed indulgently, as though upon a favored child. "I

do not believe as you do that the fates will favor us." He spoke the words calmly, holding my gaze with his. But a chill shuddered over me as he spoke. "Yet I know I shall never love another woman, Charlotte, as I love you. It will be so, whether I will it or not. I have told you already that nothing can separate our spirits, not truly—that my love for you . . ."

I pressed my finger over his lips to stop him. He fell silent as he bent over a much-folded piece of cloth to reveal a ring—small and much worn, but thickly clustered with rubies, diamonds, and emeralds. Gems in India are commonplace—incredible gems, often tragically spoiled by butchery rather than fine cutting, and cheapened by poor or gaudy settings. But this ring was old and well fashioned, and the gems cunningly set to give a subtle impression of the shades of sunset, or the shimmer of a rainbow.

I drew in my breath, stunned by its beauty and the idea that it soon would be mine. As Karan drew the ring up I noticed that it was suspended from a chain of fine gold links. He left it suspended there a moment while I gazed at it, the facets of the jewels gleaming, despite the darkness around us. Then he bent forward and fastened the chain carefully round my neck.

"We must not delude ourselves into thinking you could wear openly on your finger the gift of a—" He stopped himself. He kissed me. Against my hair, with his breath at my cheek, he said, "I love you, Charlotte. Let it be remembered that on your eighteenth birthday a man spoke his devotion to you, and his admiration of your beauty. For you are more lovely, more truly beautiful than any woman I have known."

He kissed me again, and I clung to him, then buried my face in his shoulder and wept.

The major was waiting for me. I turned Cinnamon over to his servants and strode into the quiet house unsuspecting, and the major was there.

Of course, at a nod from him I followed him into his office where he pulled on his desk lamp and bade me sit down.

"I have a most unpleasant duty before me tonight, Lottie," he began. "And I think you know what it is."

I sighed. He did not frighten me as Constance did, make my insides wither and my heart start to pound. "It is my birthday."

"All the more reason for you to behave yourself." He spoke the words wearily, as though I had displeased him greatly.

"I have done nothing wrong, nothing of which to be ashamed," I defended myself.

"You have disobeyed me." He fluttered his hands in frustration. "What you are pursuing is futile, Lottie—futile, do you hear me?"

"Why must it be? He is an educated man and an officer—"

The major brought his fist down hard on the table. "He is a native!" I had never before seen him so livid. "It was your father's express desire—his last instructions to me that under no conditions was I to consent to your marrying an Indian."

"But he died!" I cried. "He didn't understand everything. His death froze that counsel and gave it a weight that it might not otherwise have had. If he were alive . . ."

The major waved my protests aside. He wasn't listening to me! A sensation of panic rose up in my throat. "It is my life."

"I am your legal guardian, Lottie."

I knew all which that meant. I fell silent; in silence was my only dignity. He sat watching me for a few moments, fidgeting uncomfortably behind his desk.

"I should like to think you are resigned, Lottie," he said, "but I know you too well."

I said nothing. The longer I sat, the more distant I seemed from him.

"I should never forgive myself!" It was an appeal. He expected me to heed it, though he had been blind to my own.

"This is your birthday! You should be . . ." He stopped himself.

"Should be what?" He sighed and looked away from me. "Should be happy?" I said.

"You are young, Lottie. In time you will come to—"

"No!" I rose, pushing my chair back with a hard scrape. All my emotions had frozen into a terrible coldness that surged through my veins. I left the room as if in a daze. I knew he would take some action, and it would be efficient, and inexorable. Would he leave me without recourse? Without hope? I dared not entertain that possibility and give it place in my mind.

Chapter Seven

Vijaya woke me in the middle of the night. I was groggy, completely disoriented. I had fallen asleep only after hours of cold agony, and the depression of my own spirit acted like a sedative.

"Come, missysahib, come quickly! Young memsahib Hillard is dead, and no one can quiet her child."

I blinked up at her, not quite comprehending. But she took me by the shoulders and shook me, half dragging me from the bed with her insistence.

Why me? I thought dully as I let Vijaya dress me. Radha came in with a cup of strong tea, and insisted I drink it. "What can I do?" I asked her as my head began to clear. "Tell me more of what happened."

"Young wife sick for months," Radha began. Of course, I had known that. I remembered her husband vaguely, and his rather puerile self-pity.

"Yesterday morning not well. Call Dr. Fielding. He can do nothing for her. Now, before the light of the new day come to wake her, she die."

"It was the blue stage of cholera." Constance stood in my doorway. I noticed that Lucinda Jane was not in her arms.

So quickly, I thought. In a matter of hours cholera came off the victor. But then, we had seen such gruesome patterns before.

"It is the child," Constance said, watching me. "He will not be comforted." I noticed for the first time how dark and hollow her eyes were.

"What of his father?"

"The father can do nothing." Constance made a short, dismissive gesture with her hands which I understood: what good are most men in such trying circumstances?

"The child's ayah, surely his own ayah . . ."

Constance shook her head. "I have been there. He is hysterical. I have never heard such screams. Lottie, please!"

"Why were you called in the first place?" I asked, not attempting to hide my displeasure.

"We live close by. The other ladies her age are, well—young. She was not intimate with anyone, having been ill for so long."

"What difference do you think I can make?" I crossed the room, and she moved from the doorway to let me pass.

"Dr. Fielding suggested you, actually."

I glanced back at her, but she turned her eyes from me.

"You have a way with children, Lottie."

Was she thinking of her boys? Did the death of the young woman and the child's grief bring back visions of Roselyn and that other night?

I fastened a light cloak around my shoulders and walked out into the musky predawn stillness. I quickened my footsteps, but my reluctance dragged at me like a weight. Shifting my feet and turning, I realized that Vijaya was following behind me, as quiet as the shadows that trailed their way over the grass.

I heard the boy before I reached the bungalow. The sound of his cries stopped me cold. "I cannot go in there," I muttered, hoping Vijaya would hear me. But she said nothing, and made no move to detain me. I walked up to the door and lifted my hand to knock, when it slid silently open. Dr. Fielding stood before me, his thin body scarcely defined in the poorly lit entry way. He motioned me inside, then took my hand and drew me into the recess of shadows gathered about a closed doorway.

"Thank you for coming, my dear." His voice, as well as the lines of his body, revealed a state of fatigue which had long been accepted as one of the facts of his life.

"There are so many inept people in the world," he continued. "Thank heaven you're not one."

"But what can *I* do?" His reason had an effect on me; if I could just shut out the screaming that came from the back of the house.

"Every person who has approached the child so far has imposed his or her own sympathies, and horrors, upon him—and then tried to comfort the poor little creature, while only thickening the milieu of emotion. Listen to him. Be calm. Answer his questions if he has any." I don't know what expression my face wore, but his mouth twisted into a lopsided grin. "Be yourself, Lottie," he said. "That's why I sent for you."

He did not know the cruel irony that, for the first time in my life, I was in the midst of my own milieu of emotion which had nigh well undone me last night. Last night. How many hours ago was that? I followed the doctor down the dark hall toward the source of the screams.

A low lamp shed a comfortable glow over the room. I paused at the threshold. The little boy lay on his bed with his face away from me. I entered softly, closing the door behind me, and found a chair to sit upon. I don't think he knew I was there.

The great sobs had shaken his body for so long that he had to pause now and then and take in gulps of air. His little body shuddered terribly. I rose, lifted a blanket from where it lay folded at the foot of his bed, and placed it over him.

"Mother?"

At that word I began to tremble. "No, Mother has gone to heaven, remember?"

He did not speak for a moment, but gave way to the most piteous crying, though not as loud as before. I placed my hand on his cheek, then pushed his damp hair back from his forehead.

"How old are you?" I asked.

"Four," he replied.

"It's pretty tough on a lad of four to lose his mother."

"How do you know?" He moved a bit, as though at least thinking of turning round to get a look at me.

"I cannot say for certain," I replied, "since I am not you."

"I knew she was dying." He gulped on the last word and made an effort to stop crying. "We used to talk about it. She told me she would leave me and go to heaven, and I must try to be brave and help Father."

It was a deal of words to get through. He began to whimper, and drew himself into a little ball under the covers.

"What else did she say?"

He did not reply. He seemed in danger of starting off again. "You are lucky," I said. "You were able to say good-bye to your mother and tell her you love her. I was much younger, a baby, really, when my mother died."

That gave him pause. "Do you remember her?"

"A little," I replied, and that was a small lie, for I do not really remember her at all.

He could not help himself. He turned over onto his back and stared up at me. He had the darkest blue eyes I have ever seen, set in a face drained of color, so that he appeared very much like a fairy child, one of those delicate apparitions we conjure out of the mist.

"You're very beautiful," he said. "Was she as pretty as you are?"

"I believe she was even prettier."

His bottom lip began to tremble. "I'm sorry," he said. "Are you as unhappy as I am?"

I could feel my own mouth start to tremble. I reached for his hand, and he let me have it. "Yes," I told him. "Sometimes I am."

There was a sound at the door, and the doctor's head appeared. I wondered if he had been standing outside, stiff and listening, and figured that this was his moment. He carried a glass in his hand.

"Will you take the drink Dr. Fielding has prepared for you? It will help you feel better."

"Will you stay with me?" His small, warm fingers closed around mine.

"Of course. I will stay if you want me."

He drained the glass, then huddled back under the blanket. I could feel the terrible shudders that passed through his body.

Dr. Fielding leaned close and placed his hand on my head. "This will not take long."

I moved my chair beside his bed and sat there, staring straight ahead, thinking nothing, feeling nothing. The tiny hand relaxed its hold and slipped from my grasp. I must have nodded. The room was filled with the gray light of early morning when I awoke, and someone had turned the lamp off and put a blanket over me. I felt a sharp pain behind my eyes. Dr. Fielding's face shimmered, then materialized before me.

"Come, Lottie," he said gently. "I'll take you home to your bed."

I resisted his attempt to raise me. "I must be here when he wakes."

"I will see to it," he promised. "The lad will sleep for hours, probably the better part of the day."

I let him lead me through the dew-cold morning, Vijaya trailing behind. It felt good to think of nothing, to crawl into my cool bed and shut my eyes, as though all that had happened during the past twenty-four hours was only a dream.

I awoke feeling groggy still, and at first not remembering what had happened. Vijaya entered the room, as though she had been waiting outside the door for the sounds of my waking.

"There is time for you to bathe and dress; the child sleeps peacefully still."

I was grateful. I gave myself over to her ministrations and tried not to think. A sense of gloom, almost of hopelessness had settled over me, which my tired spirits could not resist. When Domingo brought in a hot dish of *kedgeree,* I ate with more relish than I would have thought possible. The morning was cool. I could hear the complaining "cheel! cheel! cheel!" of the small kite bird, and the soft babbling of the sandy brown *hudhuds* on the bungalow roof. Mischief, the boys' monkey, was happily scratching away in the garden outside my window. I thought how I must speak to Radha about him. Where was the monkey boy who had been appointed to keep track of the little fellow?

Domingo entered the room again, but not to clear the dishes away. He carried a small tray upon which rested a letter—a slender envelope with one word only—"Charlotte"—written across it. He held it out to me. "This arrived by messenger, missysahib."

I realized I was not breathing properly. With the tips of my fingers I lifted the missive from the tray, and Domingo bowed himself out. I met Vijaya's eyes, and she reluctantly followed him. Alone now, I tore at the seal with trembling fingers and drew out the single sheet.

"Charlotte," it began, with no formal salutation or term of endearment. "Several men of our company have been selected for special duty. We leave early tomorrow. I shall explain when I see you—tonight, as usual?"

It was signed merely "K." No other identifying marks were on it. I placed the letter back into its envelope and slipped it inside the deep pocket of my skirt. "As usual" meant anywhere between nine and ten o'clock at our spot down by the farthest end of the park, where the Hooghly wound like a thin, mottled ribbon bordered by green banks and low, stunted trees.

I opened the door and walked out into the hallway. Vijaya materialized at my side. "Let us go check on the progress of the child," I said, and she followed me out. We walked the short distance to the Hillard home in silence. *Special duty,* I thought. *That could mean anything, and anywhere.* I did not have to guess who had initiated this order, or what the motives behind it might be.

Major Hillard himself opened the door to us.

"Miss Simmons," he said, affording me a slight bow. "I was just going out. How may I be of assistance?"

"It is I who have come to be of assistance. Your son . . ." I stammered a bit, realizing I did not even know the boy's name.

"He is sleeping peacefully. Dr. Fielding is with him." His eyes looked dull; he seemed unable to fix their gaze on anything, or at least, he would not look directly at me.

"Good. He has not awakened yet. I promised him I would be here."

Geoffrey Hillard managed to look amazed despite himself, and I controlled an errant urge to laugh lightly. *Heavens, Lottie!* I chided myself. *The man has just lost his wife.*

"That is altogether unnecessary, my dear! The doctor can manage. We would not think of imposing—"

"I gave my word, sir." I spoke the words with a slow, deliberate emphasis. "I am in the habit of keeping my word."

"I see." He arched an eyebrow at me, and the long mustache, which partly obscured his expression, quivered. Was he annoyed?

"By all means, then." With a sweeping gesture that was slightly mocking he stood back from the door, making way for my entrance. As I passed close to him I felt his brown eyes move over me with an exacting appraisal. I looked up and this time forced his eyes to meet mine.

"You have a rare and sensitive little boy," I said, hoping he could read the sincerity behind my words and not think them empty, given in view of their joint bereavement.

"He is fortunate to find such a sympathetic and dedicated friend as yourself," he answered.

A strange reply, I thought. Was he being caustic, goaded by his own pain? Or might he sincerely envy the fact that his son, being a child, could grieve openly, and be openly comforted, while he, a man, must hide behind his unimpassioned British exterior, and keep the stiff upper lip expected of him and his kind?

❧

Dr. Fielding, at least, was pleased to see me. "Winston is the boy's name," he informed me, "and he has stirred and moaned a time or two this past hour."

"I can manage," I assured him. "It is your turn to rest now."

He smiled wryly. "I have other patients waiting."

I put my hand on his arm. "Will you be all right?"

"Dear girl," he answered, working to hide his pleasure, "this is business as usual for me, nothing out of the ordinary."

"Well, I do not see how you survive."

I watched him go, feeling far more empty and uncertain than I had let on. I sat by the child's bed for the better part of an hour, penning a letter to Hugh and Arthur, before I became aware of a vague stirring of the bedclothes and looked up to see Winston watching me, his blue eyes stained as violet as the sea when a storm stirs her.

"You look better," I said. "Do you feel rested?" I kept any tone of false gaiety from my voice; he would be able to see through that, I knew. "Do you feel hungry?"

He shook his head.

"Perhaps later," I said, dismissing the matter.

"What are you doing?" He crawled on his knees to the edge of the bed and peered at the pages in my lap with an open curiosity.

"I am writing to Hugh and Arthur, my brothers. They have gone back to England to school."

"Do you miss them?"

"Dreadfully," I admitted. "And the more so because I sense they are less than happy with their lives there."

A small scowl drew his dark eyebrows together. "Cannot you send for them, then?"

"No, they are English lads like yourself, and like yourself they are expected to endure their lot bravely and without complaint."

He nodded solemnly; such a concept was not new to him.

"They are not my real brothers," I amended, noting his

solemn expression. "So they are not motherless like ourselves."

The implied camaraderie of my statement pleased him. He sidled closer.

"We are much alike, you and I," I said thoughtfully. "Perhaps we might help one another."

He knew exactly what I meant. The intelligence behind his eyes was almost startling.

"I should like to help you," he replied.

"Good." I rose as if to leave. *I shall need more help than I'd like to think of,* I mused grimly. "You wash and eat, and do whatever is required of you this day," I said slowly. "It is late already, and I will most probably not be able to return."

Winston looked down, unwilling to let me see his disappointment.

"But I shall be back in the morning. And we shall make arrangements to see one another daily."

He knew he could trust me. "All right," he agreed, though his voice was very small. As I turned to leave he slid off the bed and buried his face against me, with his little arms wrapped round my legs. We stood together that way for a few minutes until his ayah entered the room and gently pried him away.

The night was dark. This was India's winter, if one could call it such. But the season was early yet, and the air pleasantly cool and invigorating as I rode Cinnamon down the long park toward the murmuring river. The major had not been home when I left, and I had merely told Constance that I must get away. I wondered how much she had been told of my "offenses," realizing uneasily that I could expect no sympathy from that quarter. Major Reid, of course, need no longer concern himself. He had made arrangements to send the offender away. And in his mind, that settled the matter.

Karan was waiting. A small lantern rested on a raised slab of stone where he had pushed the tall, matted grasses away. He had placed a thick woven rug over the cold stone bench. But he was not sitting. He stood in the shadows watching, and waiting for me. At first no word passed between us. He tethered Cinnamon beside his horse, his movements deliberate, unhurried, as if we had all the time in the world. I sat and watched him, trying to mark precisely his smooth, easy gait, the way he moved his long, slender hands, the cast of his face in the half-light, and the solemn peace of his eyes that looked out steadily and untroubled upon the horrors we were facing.

"Where is he sending you?" I demanded, my nerves jangled by waiting.

"A small contingent of men is being posted to Patna, near the Dunwar Pass. Some of the villages near there have requested assistance."

"For what reason?" I asked.

"The reason is of no matter," Karan replied. "What matters is that I am going, Charlotte, and this is the end."

I could not move; I could not respond to him. He sat as still as a statue beside me, his eyes never leaving my face.

"You will return," I said at last.

"Perhaps—and, if so, briefly. You know the major will see to it that I am reassigned elsewhere."

"Has he told you as much?"

An expression of mingled contempt and bitterness played over his features. "He would not stoop to deal with me directly, Charlotte." A shudder passed over his frame. I leaned instinctively toward him; I felt him tense and draw back.

"We had our farewell the night of your birthday," he said, and this time his tone became hushed and gentle. "Surely you knew it, dearest, as well as I."

My fingers plucked through the lace at my throat, seeking the feel of the thin gold chain that rested against my skin. "We are to accept this? Allow them to dictate our lives for us?" I stood facing him, trembling all over. I could no longer sit still.

"We have no choice!" His voice was still maddeningly level, but the compacted emotion it carried had the force of a blow.

"We will find ways—there must be ways . . ."

Karan rose with lithe swiftness and gripped me hard by the shoulders. His face was only inches from mine.

"Charlotte, listen to me! I am dead to you—and you are dead to me! So the gods have decreed it."

"No! So John Company has decreed it."

"In India, for all practical purposes, they are one and the same."

He loosened his grip. His hands fell from my shoulders, and he took a step or two back—deliberate steps, deliberately distancing himself from me. With that searing cruelty so common to youth, I shouted back at his silence.

"You would give me up so easily? Take the coward's way out?" I could see his whole body begin to tremble, but I plunged on anyway. "You will walk out of here, without ever touching me, never to see me again?"

"It is the only way. Anything else—leads to madness."

I threw my head back, but whatever rebuttal had been brewing in my hot brain froze on my lips. Karan's solid brown eyes had melted into pools of agony. His misery rendered me helpless and stupid. I stood staring across the dark space at him, my breath coming in sobs now, saying nothing at all.

"So be it." Karan's voice carried the echoes of doom as he spoke the sentence. He walked to where the horses were tethered and untied Cinnamon, then held him for me to mount. "I will follow in a few minutes," he said. "It will be better that way."

A panic rose up in me, a panic so woven into my need for him that I did not see how I could bear it. He was sending me forth, with a slap on Cinnamon's withers, to face the next moment, the next day, the next eternity—and I could not do it! I had not the power within me. Yet at the last moment, my pride—another characteristic youth possesses in abundance—came to my aid.

I can be as brave and noble as you are! I thought fiercely. Before I knew it, the big horse was cantering away, and Karan stood behind me, and I could not properly turn myself round, nor call out to him, nor . . . My head was spinning. The distance between us lengthened. The night became as black and as dumb as the pain I carried inside.

CHAPTER EIGHT

I SURVIVED. ONE DOES, DESPITE THE PAIN. People develop a capacity for pain, I discovered; brain as well as body compensates and adapts, and life goes on—perhaps without meaning or purpose; but it goes on, ne'ertheless.

The funeral for Judith Hillard was held on the fourth day following her death. By that time her son, Winston, and I were fast friends. But I was not there the dread morning to prevent him from slipping out of the house and running after his father, who was about to climb stiffly into the funeral carriage.

"Poor Papa," the child cried, winding his arms about his father's legs. "Please let me come, too! I will hold your hand tight and keep you from crying."

Major Hillard's stout steward carried the boy back into the house. I became furious when I heard. Yet the servants' talk had it that the father's face was wet with tears—the first anyone had observed since the doctor closed his wife's eyes and pronounced her dead.

I attended the funeral, though I would have preferred being at home in company of the chief mourner. The gloom of such occasions is always depressing to me. I had spoken little to either Constance or the major since my last meeting with Karan. Perhaps they sensed my silent animosity; I do not know, and I did not then care. It provoked me immensely that I had to learn from Karan where he was going; yet I would have died before asking the major, or even vaguely fishing for hints. The terrible foreboding that constantly pressed upon me was a mingling of the two tragedies I was involved in, and I found it difficult to separate them in my mind. I suppose I lavished my frustrated attention upon Winston, the only possible recipient. And that, as it turned out, was fortunate for the boy, though it served to create far more serious consequences for me.

The day following the funeral, I invited Winston to our bungalow for tea. He came holding onto his ayah's hand and looking a little uncertain. But the surprise I had prepared for him was one that could not be resisted; I was certain of that. We sat in the warmest part of the garden, away from the shade of the banyan, where the high sun could strike us and heat the chill air. Constance joined us briefly, with Radha at her elbow, carrying a squirming Lucinda in her arms. Constance used for excuse the fact that the child might catch cold in the fresh air. But I cannot say I was sorry when she hurried inside with her poor, pampered infant. I instructed Vijaya to go in search of Soobratta, the monkey boy. He came into the garden a few moments later, Mischief jumping and chattering, and tugging at the woven string he was bound to.

Winston slid out of his seat and was upon the monkey in an instant, his own eyes as wide and bright as the creature's. Mischief regarded him solemnly, his small head cocked at a curious angle. Then, pulling his lips back from his teeth, he shrieked a shrill, short note of approval as he reached one furry arm out and batted at Winston's chest gleefully.

"That's Mischief's signal that he wants you to play with him," I explained. Winston glanced back at me. "It's all right," I assured him. "Go wherever you like, as long as you stay in the gardens."

How is it that children *know* how to play? Is there some natural instinct built into them that fades away or simply ceases to function with the onset of maturity? Watching the boy and the small beast together, I was amazed at the similarity of behavior between this small, bereaved child and my confident and aggressive young brothers. They raced through the tall grass, scrambled through hedges, and swung from the low-hanging branches of the banyan, communicating with one another as only children and animals can do. I realized how much I missed Hugh and Arthur, and I shuddered at how dismal things now had become. Constance, still obsessed by her fears, lived in the dread confinements she had set for herself. Major Reid lived an officer's life, which included only minimal hours here. And myself? I had glimpsed happiness and believed I was on the verge of a life of my own. Now dreariness, like a kind of hopelessness, dragged my spirits and dulled all my senses: beauty and song, and my sensations of pleasure in mere living, had ceased to be.

But I had found some way to aid the small motherless boy, and that pleased me well. With an assured promise that he could visit again the next day, and each day thereafter, Winston suffered his ayah to take him back home. I went into the house, but the rooms seemed to stifle me. A restlessness worse than my lethargy goaded me, until I sent Vijaya to tell Constance that I would be taking Cinnamon out for a ride. We paced the broad avenue where the officers and their ladies paraded. I kept my eyes discreetly down or staring vacantly ahead. I forced myself to the routine, for where else could I go? Every spot of beauty and solitude the station or the nearby countryside harbored was vivid with memories; I could not hazard those memories and the emotions they stirred. Besides, as a general rule young ladies did not ride out of an evening alone. A servant or two, perhaps as many as five depending upon the lady's station, would accompany her. Servants were a fact of life in India almost worse than the insects, the dry, hot winds, or the relentless rains. Privacy was an unknown commodity, a luxury we could not even imagine. Perhaps that was why women like Constance could lose themselves. The boredom, the stifling routine of days made even the most inventive mind, the most energetic spirit have to contrive things to do.

I rode round and round until my brain felt muddled and dull again, and the terrible passion was spent. I pointed

Cinnamon's head homeward. The wide sky had turned slate, and a chill wind fretted the grass at our feet. I wondered how long, day following day, I could live life like this.

A dance, a pleasant evening out. I had no excuse at all to avoid it. I went, not so much to please the major, but to avoid conflict and the lonely boredom I dreaded. This would be a rather grand affair, since the governor-general was to be in attendance. I dressed with extra care, wearing the watered blue silk I save for special occasions, with pearls at my throat. I even allowed Radha, who has a gift for such matters, to pile my hair high, with cascading curls flowing down from the crown of my head and hugging the line of my chin and the curve of my cheeks. It was an attractive style and served to accentuate my delicate bones and deep-set eyes—the eyes of my mother. I felt I had the dark, expressive eyes of her race, rather than English eyes, which sometimes bulge and often seem to be cutting right through one with a piercing, inquisitive gaze. I felt pretty; the flush of youth and the flood of emotion that can make one's head feel light ran warm through my veins. It pleased me to notice that men's eyes turned to look at me, either discreetly or boldly. I savored the sense of power it gave me, which is so heady to youth; I savored it all the more because I knew how empty and tasteless it was. Yet it was something tangible, something to possess, and I determined to cling to it, as long as the only thing I desired was denied to me.

We dined at six. The verandas of the governor-general's great colonnaded house were closed in with branches and an array of exotic blossoms: jasmine, hibiscus, and oleander. Vases overflowing with roses and sweet peas adorned every table, and the effect *was* impressive, especially with the dozens upon dozens of tall lamps, which had been put up to light the vast room.

There had been racing earlier in the day, and the governor-general had put up some rather elaborate silver cheroot boxes for prizes. So several of the gentlemen swaggered in, making a point of lighting their friends' cigars in order to show off their prizes which, indirectly, boasted of their equestrian prowess as well. I found it all a bit tedious and was stifling a yawn as discreetly as I could when a voice at my elbow said, "I, myself, never indulge, Miss Simmons, so you need not take pains to hide your boredom from me."

I looked up to see Major Hillard actually smiling at me, his long mustache seeming to curl up with the effect of it. *Who has contrived to seat him next to me?* I thought fleetingly, but I answered him smoothly, "You are a gentleman, sir, to cover my offenses so kindly." Then I laughed lightly, because I was uncomfortable with the way he stared at me.

"Geoffrey finds horses a frivolous waste of a man's money." Major Reid thumped his old friend companionably on the back, coming to my rescue without knowing it.

We ate sardines from the Mediterranean, salmon from Scotland, and half a dozen other delicacies, while the band played Haydn's *London* symphonies and selections from Beethoven's *Ninth.* I gave myself over to the music and used it as an excuse to ignore the present company. But when coffee was served and the display of fireworks started, I was forced for decency's sake to converse with Major Hillard, who had still contrived to remain in our party.

"What other pursuits claim your interest in lieu of racing and betting?" I asked.

"I am a great reader," he answered, "and think it not untoward to boast that I possess one of the largest libraries in India."

I was impressed, though not inclined to show it.

"I am a reader as well," I confessed.

"I am pleased to find a young woman who knows the value of thought well expressed and language . . ." he hesitated.

"For the sake of sheer beauty," I added.

His smile became one of sincere delight. "It is a pity," he said. "My wife would have suffered far less if she had been able to find enjoyment in such pleasures."

I thought his tone was a bit reflective, with perhaps even a tenderness to it.

"India is a hard place for women, especially young women," I said.

"Have you found it so?"

"I have no other comparison. You must know my history—"

A particularly magnificent display of color illuminated the sky with shades that would rival the most vivid sunset, and seemed to stain the very atmosphere. It served to interrupt us, and I afterward took care to turn the conversation, not wishing to resume any bent that would lead to intimate discussion of myself. Beauty—disturbing in itself to the overly sensitive spirit—now drew from the very core of me a longing for Karan. He should be here by my side. It was blasphemous to drink in this wonder and not share it with him. And it was sinful, a wretched waste, to see my own loveliness reflected in the admiring gaze of strangers, and to know that the one who loved me truly and dearly was not here to partake.

The fireworks ended, but the dancing would go on until midnight. As the music started up again Major Hillard bowed slightly, by way of requesting permission, then drew me into his arms. I shuddered. It was not that his touch was repulsive to me—but it was not the touch that I longed for. If I was stiff in his hold, if he sensed my reluctance, it was nothing to me. At that point I cared only to make it through the remainder of the evening and reach the retreat of my room, where I could weep out my misery into the darkness, undisturbed.

The following day as I sat at tea with Constance, a messenger arrived with a parcel that had my name written on it. My mind was blank as I picked it up and began to unwrap it. Who could possibly be the sender? The papers fell back to reveal a leather-bound copy of *Ivanhoe* by Sir Walter Scott. I held it a moment, enjoying the feel of it in my hands. There was no card enclosed, but on the end sheet of the volume was written an inscription. I read the message to myself, wishing Constance had not been with me when the offering arrived.

"What is it?" she insisted, bending over me.

"It appears to be from Major Hillard," I said. "A gift."

"What has he written?"

I glanced up at her face and had the oddest impression that she was pleased.

"He writes: 'You of all women would enjoy this. I fancy you possess many of the qualities of the book's heroine. May the reading bring you pleasure. Yours respectfully, G. Hillard.'"

"How very nice," Constance chirped vacuously, shifting Lucinda Jane to her other knee.

I thought it very odd, though I did not say so.

"Let me take the child," I suggested, hoping also to turn the subject. "We'll go for a walk round the gardens."

"It is too early in the day yet," she responded, without even thinking. "The sun is too oppressive—"

"The air is cool and the sun but pleasantly warm," I urged, but Constance shook her head.

"Radha and I will take her out later," she replied.

I placed the book on the table and rose with deliberation. "I am both dependable and cautious. I will take special care with Lucy. Let me have her," I said.

Her eyes met mine. I thought they looked as worn and faded as the rest of her. "Ten minutes won't hurt, I suppose," she said, as she dropped her gaze.

The child was a beauty still, and her nature had remained agreeable, despite the unhealthy pampering she was accustomed to. I carried her in my arms, and she gazed with wide, unblinking interest at all around her. We sat on the stone bench beneath the tamarind tree and I sang her a tune. She screwed up her little bow mouth as if to sing with me, and curled her miniature fist around one of my fingers, holding on tight. But I was aware that Constance stood behind the curtain at the drawing room window, watching. And when Radha came out to fetch the child it had been only eight minutes by the pocket watch which I wore.

The routine of my days now included a visit from Winston, which—proving the narrowness of my life—I looked forward to. I cajoled Constance into allowing Radha and me to drag out some of the boys' old toys and books for him. What times we had sailing boats on the trickle of stream that ran at the back of the bungalow, catching lizards, playing tigers and lions, with Mischief consigned to the role of the wild beast which we so cleverly stalked. Winston was a bright boy, if a little withdrawn in nature. At times a faraway look, perhaps a sadness connected with the loss of his mother, would dull his blue eyes, and he would retreat into a world peopled only with his own shadows and longings and fears.

I read the book Mr. Hillard sent, wondering what he thought he had seen in me to make him believe me to be anything like the gentle, self-effacing Jewish girl of the novel. Did he sense that my own fires burned as low and as faithfully as her own? What romantic notion did he weave to his own liking?

I read other books borrowed from his library. There were even times when he would walk over of an evening with some offering he believed I would particularly enjoy. He thanked me often and unstintingly for the influence I had on his son. Considering the man's nature, this was a generous gesture which I appreciated. He was a strange man, disciplined to a fault, as many of the English are, and reticent in the expression of anything touching upon emotion, but I was accustomed to that.

Christmas day came and went. We observed the season as Englishmen in India do, confined as we are by heathen customs and a heathen climate. The true import of the day, namely the sacrifice of the Son of God for the souls of all men, seemed little mentioned nor taken into consideration. Oh, we attended service in our small stone chapel and sang a few hymns. But once outside, life went on as usual. The men had their games and their fine wines, the women their conversations and their fine dresses. I had nothing but a haunting memory, and a sense of loss, as keen as the winds on the desert, blowing my soul bare. I think I felt the need of a savior, the need of a love that could transcend the cruelties and hypocrisies of men.

I had Cinnamon saddled and rode him to the cemetery, which was understandably vacant and silent on this festive day. I did not have to close my eyes to see Karan before me, his face a mask of serenity, his eyes reflecting the fires that burned more deeply and surely than mine.

"Where are you?" I asked aloud. "What will happen to you?" Only the blackbirds gave cry, lonely and mocking. All else about me was still. Then his words came back to me: *If we were to be parted this very night, never to meet in this life again, I would still love you . . .* I choked on the words, as if they tore through my own throat. *I would still love you with the same joy and devotion that flow through me right now.*

Karan's words were poetry because his soul was poetry. I dropped down on my knees, leaning my head against the cold gray stone that bore Roselyn's name. I let the tears which had been checked for weeks work their ragged course through me. I arose weak and drained, with a dozen questions in my mind, but no answers. I rode back to the house. As I walked up the back steps, smelling still of fresh air and horse flesh, Vijaya met me, her manner nervous and her color flushed.

"Major Hillard waits in the parlor for you, this half hour and more," she stammered. When she saw my annoyance and the flash in my eyes, she said, "You refuse to see what all others know, missysahib."

"And what is that?" I snapped, pushing rudely past her. But she grabbed my wrist to detain me, patient as usual, but with that quiet power many self-contained women possess. "That the major courts you," she stated, as though speaking to a child or a simpleton. "He courts you! You can no longer ignore that, or pretend not to see."

She dropped my wrist, turned, and walked before me. I lowered my head, as though warding off an unexpected blow, and followed docilely behind.

Chapter Nine

The dream was nonsensical—only the suggestion of fire, white-hot and searing, traveling up my own body from the soles of my feet to the tingling tips of my fingers and the crown of my head. But that was not all: an incoherent agony screamed out of a black void, empty save for two lurid coals that burned amber and brass and scarlet—and they seemed to be the source of the pain that woke me with a start of terror.

I pushed the bedclothes away from my soaked and trembling body. I am not given much to dream, as some people are. I stared into the darkness and tried to discount the images that still scorched me with their intensity.

At last I arose. Though the sky was gray still, with that pale cast of light that precedes the dawn, I knew I would sleep no more that night, so why toss in my bed? No one heard me; even Vijaya was blessedly absent. I dressed by myself and slipped noiselessly into the garden. There the birds anointed the morning with melody: the warbling tailor birds, the sweet-throated bulbuls, and the noisome hawk cuckoos, called *popiyas*. The blending of sound was magnificent. I closed my eyes and listened while the cool morning rushed over me, heaven mingling with heaven, and I but a mortal, and not a very wise one at that. I sat a long time, silent observer and partaker, before I rose with a sigh and went back into the house.

I came to find myself, over the course of the months, sitting on half a dozen ladies' committees with Constance, or rather, in Constance's place. To these meetings she could easily have brought Lucinda Jane. But other women brought infants who might prove to be carriers of some dread disease. So seldom, very seldom, could Constance be persuaded to set her fears aside and meet with her friends. I'm sure the women looked upon me as a lukewarm substitute; Constance had been one of them for years and was a recognized leader. I was untried, unmarried—uninitiated in every essential way. Besides that, I was reticent to a fault. I kept my own counsel in ways most women relished in expressing theirs; I quite plainly did not fit in. They put up with me, condescending kindly, blissfully unaware that, from my view of things, I was condescending to their ways as well.

This morning, ten of us gathered in Gwen Abbott's parlor to finalize details for the Fancy Fair, which was to be held in a fortnight. The various booths had already garnered a respectable accumulation of piecework and handcrafted goods. We were chatting over tea when Gwen, still blinking brightly, chirped, like the mischievous kite bird, "Have you ladies heard the ghastly news? This morning they brought a soldier into hospital who had been attacked by a tiger." She held up her dainty, gloved hand. "Do not fear—it was not in our vicinity. A small contingent of Ethan's men had been detailed to repair roads and bridges near Patna. Apparently there was a man-eating tiger terrorizing those parts."

We all knew what that meant. In some areas where tigers are numerous, they wax bold enough to prowl the haunts of men in broad day. They know no fear, and it is not easy to stop them. It is not uncommon for a tiger who develops a taste for human flesh to carry away a man or child daily—week after week, month after month, until he is stopped.

The ladies shuddered. Gwen, enjoying the suspense she was creating, went on.

"Anyway, our soldiers went out to track the beast, and it seems the tiger pounced upon one of them and carried him off by his leg, dragging the poor man through the jungle—can you imagine?"

Anne Thomas put her slender hand to her slender throat, and her white face turned a shade more pale. I was trembling inside. With the tips of my fingers I touched the stretch of my gown beneath which rested the small jeweled ring. Even as Gwen said it, I knew.

"The man was a sepoy, a native—thank heaven for that much."

All the ladies breathed easier, but my breath was choking me!

"Does he live?" someone asked, through the ringing in my ears.

"Yes, I told you they brought him to hospital, and will probably move him to Calcutta after a few days. He's been terribly maimed, and will most probably lose his leg, so Ethan believes. Pity, isn't it?" she concluded. "Even for a sepoy."

The ladies clucked and murmured, attempting to smooth their ruffled feathers, to still the thrill of fear Gwen had stirred. I stood up, awkwardly, I suppose, leaning against the table for support, with both my hands twisted into white-knuckled knots.

"I must leave," I said. "At once." I nodded to my hostess, then turned and walked out of the room—somehow—without stumbling, or falling a heap at their feet. I was aware, through the mist of pain that blinded me, that dignity was my best protectress, my only shield. I did not wait for the startled servants to saddle Cinnamon, but rode with only a blanket for padding, taking shortcuts through fields where the rooks cried, and down thin, dust-clogged lanes, until I reached the low, colorless building where the ill and wounded were kept.

I was not thinking; I was not feeling, really, but moving by instinct alone. Some sort of sentry posted at the door stared agape, but I swept past too swiftly for him to question me.

"The native soldier who was brought in this morning,

where has he been placed?" I demanded of a white-aproned nurse.

"Miss, I do not—"

"Tell me at once!" I ground the words out between my teeth. "Else I shall find him myself."

"Third room on the left, straight ahead," she answered. And now her eyes were studying me, and she was forming thoughts of her own. I swept away from her, my dignity a bit tattered but still holding me up.

The door was shut. I pushed it open and slid in with scarcely a sound. The room was dim, blinds drawn against the sunlight. I glanced over a row of five beds imprinted with the shapes of five men, broken and motionless, and emptied by pain. The last bed was half-enclosed by a curtain of netting. I moved down the room. Not even my skirts made a rustle, and the sleeping men did not seem to breathe. I drew back the netting, the grip of my fingers crumpling the frail covering.

Karan lay stretched and silent, a thin shadow of his former self, and nearly too long for the bed, which did not look as though it contained him comfortably. His warm, healthy skin was wan, his eyes closed, but the lines of his face were drawn tightly with pain. The bedclothes concealed his limbs and the horrible damage that must have been done there. There was the stale smell of suffering, death's grim harbinger. Creeping closer, I made out a long red gash that trailed a jagged path down his cheek. I kissed the tips of my fingers and touched them to it.

"Enough of this nonsense!" A gruff voice spoke at my elbow, and I jumped visibly. "The lad's sedated and would not know you from a crocodile."

"Or a tiger?" I turned and looked into two narrow gray eyes that were tired and bloodshot. "Thank heaven it is you!"

Dr. Fielding gave me his hands, though I crushed them in a grip that made the muscles near his mouth twitch. "Really, Charlotte, this is no place for you." He turned as he spoke, half pulling me along with him. When we approached the door, I drew back.

"Will you tell me all that happened," I whispered, "if I agree to go out with you?"

"I've no business," he protested. "You know what the major will do to me if he finds out."

"He will find out," I said, standing my ground and pulling my hands back from his. "And he is my problem, not yours. I shall not leave this room—"

"All right, all right. You know I cannot oppose you, Lottie." He gave me a sad little smile that struck more fear into me than all Gwen Abbott's thoughtless words had. I followed him out into the hall.

We walked halfway back to the entrance where a cluster of chairs was planted. "Sit down," he instructed, "and drink this." He poured liquid from a pot which stood on a nearby table and handed me a full cup of a brown, rich smelling liquid. "I will be candid if you think you can bear it."

I nodded, wondering what my face looked like. "From you," I said, "more than any other." His sagging face softened. "I have heard the bare outline over tea at Gwen Abbott's," I added.

He grimaced. "Very well, I shall fill in the rest. This tiger was vicious and had grown exceedingly bold, and the natives were terrified." His narrow mouth twisted. "Those details are pretty commonplace. The turn of events came when the men were out searching and your young friend here—"

"His name is Karan."

"Very well, when Karan here got separated from the rest of the men. Apparently they had seen no big game at all, no tracks of the tiger, and were not concerned until their companion failed to show up. When they finally decided to track him quite some time had elapsed, and it took them hours to find him."

I shivered and wrapped my fingers around the warm tea mug.

"When they discovered signs of his being dragged through the undergrowth for nearly a mile—well, they did not expect to find much of him." He put his hand out to steady me.

"What did they find?"

"The man had not a revolver, but a shotgun with him! And, mind you, what good was that? He's an amazing fellow, Lottie. He kept a cool head, knowing he would get in one shot and one shot only, and it had best find its mark. Somehow he contrived to point the weapon at the tiger's heart, take long and steady—and I suppose excruciating aim—"

I set my cup and saucer down with a clatter and clenched my hands into fists at my sides. The doctor eyed me cautiously but continued his narrative.

"The shot went true and the tiger fell dead, but the poor lad lay half-crushed beneath him, with his knee locked so securely in the jaws of the beast that his friends had to break the knee before they could free him."

I shook my head, trying to dislodge the images his words called forth so vividly. "How is he now?"

"It was some time before he received medical attention—"

"Can you save his leg?"

"Some think not, but I tend to be more hopeful. What infection he had is responding well to treatment. We've cleaned the wound well. Some of the tendons are injured, but if the tissue re-forms and—"

"Will he ever walk again?"

"If we save the leg. But not well, Lottie, not—"

"Not well enough for the army?" I spoke the words so quietly that I wondered if I had only thought them. "Just the excuse Major Reid is looking for. Will he cashier Karan out, Dr. Fielding?"

"I expect that he will." The doctor ran a finger along his narrow chin line, then rubbed his bleared eyes.

"A hero, if he were a white man; a has-been because he's a native."

The doctor looked at me and his eyes told the truth of it: *Not only because he is a native, but because he is a native who has taken an interest in you.*

"He has suffered much pain?"

"He has suffered much pain—bravely."

"Of course," I replied. "I will go to him now."

"You'll do no such thing."

I rose and, leaning close, planted a kiss on his forehead. "I shall write a note to my ayah. Have you someone here who can deliver it? Good." I began walking, and he shuffled resignedly behind me. "Vijaya can handle Constance, and I shall handle the major."

"He may not wake for hours," the doctor warned me.

"I will wait."

As we approached the room, he reached out a hand to detain me. "Lottie, dear . . ." I responded to his gaze reluctantly. "I am not concerned for Ralph's sake; I believe you know that. But when all this is through . . ." He waved his arm in the direction of the closed door, and his face looked miserable. "It will only be more wretched for you," he said, "because in the end you will still have to walk away."

"I know that," I replied, facing him squarely, hoping that with his doctor's discernment he could not tell that my head was ringing again and that my legs felt weak and rubbery. I closed my hand over the doorknob.

"I'll come back to check on you often," he promised, and his voice held such pity, such tender concern, that it nearly undid me. He turned and walked off down the hall, and I entered the small room, where all the cruelty of the world seemed waiting to crush and mock me.

Vijaya brought me books and a drawing pad and pencils, as I had instructed. Also her tea apparatus. "I will be here if you have need of me," she insisted, indicating a spot in the bare corridor. I did not try to argue. I sat by the bed watching Karan's face until my vision blurred. I could hear the high, trumpeting shouts of elephants along the river. Was another company of men moving out? All these lives, all these individual hearts beating, and only one among all of them that really mattered to me.

The sun was setting. I stood by the square of window and watched the sky turn amethyst with streaks and stars of ruby and topaz running through it, like the sparkling jewels on a rajah's robe. The colors sank to a deep violet-laced azure before the pigments faded to a gray as ashen as tears. I turned, and the major stood in the doorway watching me.

"Well, Lottie."

I moved away from the window and took up my post by the bed. But I did not sit—that would put me at a disadvantage. He moved closer, until we stood facing one another. His eyes were as stern as his face, and that frightened me.

"This is your work," I said.

"Rubbish," he answered.

"I am not one of your men," I replied. "This is not 'risks of the service, to be expected, keep a stiff upper lip' and all that nonsense." I drew a deep breath, knowing I must keep my voice even and reasonable.

"What are you getting at, Lottie?"

"I am your *daughter.*" His eyes wavered ever so slightly. "I need you as a daughter needs you."

"I can do nothing here."

"You! You can do everything here—beyond what you've already done!"

The timbre of my voice had risen; I clenched my hands at my sides.

"Look here, Lottie. This entire affair is an embarrassment to me. You must realize that. If you had not run straight from Gwen Abbott's house to this place—whatever possessed you, girl! By tonight I'll warrant the whole post will know of it."

"That remains your prime consideration." I had myself under control again, though my heart was aching, longing to see him soften toward me. I should not have tried to open up to him; I had too much pain as it was.

"What if it were Roselyn?" I asked. "Your own daughter. What if she fell in love with the wrong man?"

"Lottie, you do not understand . . ."

My words were just that, only words to him. He was a man accustomed to authority and influence, he *would not* be beguiled into entertaining feelings that might possess power to undermine him!

"You compromise all that I am by your presence here; I believe you understand that."

"Such is not my purpose."

He inclined his head a little, like an old dog sniffing the wind. "Whatever your purposes are, they shall come to naught, my dear."

"It need not be so."

"It *is so.*" He stood glaring at me with that presence that must have intimidated many a young cadet or sepoy. "I could have you forcibly removed, Charlotte."

It was a definite threat. He was playing his last card because he knew he held the trump, and he was bored with the game.

"I should make you regret it," I said, raising my chin a notch higher. He couldn't help gaping a little. We had never come to such stubborn cross-purposes before.

"Allow me to stay," I suggested. "Allow me to care for him—now—when he needs me . . ."

He began an imperious wave of his hand.

"I will ask no more." I pushed back a tendril of hair that had fallen over my forehead. My chin, at its awkward tilt, trembled. "After that . . ." I continued with deliberation, "I will ask no more of you."

I could see that he was scrutinizing me carefully. I did not realize that I was crying until a tear slid down my cheek. I wiped at my eyes with the back of my hand.

"My dear . . ."

I said nothing, and he continued to study me. I knew his fine mind was working, with deliberation and precision. I could not have guessed as to the state of his heart.

"You've never caused us any trouble before this day." He was remembering. And in my case, that was good. "And you've been a real trooper through this—difficulty with Constance."

I began to relax just a little. The major was nothing if not fair.

"All right. We shall strike our bargain." His eyes drove into mine, and there was no lenity in them. "I have your word?"

"You have my word."

"Very good." He would leave details to others. His work here was done. He strode out of the room with no further word to me. I knew I had just won an amazing victory—and I had just lost everything. I sank into the chair and covered my face with my hands. But the tears would not come. I stared into the gathering darkness, engulfed in my own void of pain.

The vigil was a nightmarish tedium of pain. Karan did not stir. The night shadows played along his sunken cheeks and pale brow, until I fancied he looked more like a corpse than a living man—he looked like a stranger to me. *What am I doing here?* I asked, staring at his face until my eyes burned. *What is this man to me?* But I knew. The inner voice, though cowed and silenced, still recognized the sacred knowledge that had brought me here—the force within me that was stronger than weariness and pride, stronger than doubt and fear.

I freed the slender chain so that it rested outside my bodice, and the ring, with its shifting lights and colors, sat like a cool stone in the hollow of my neck. I drank Vijaya's tea and picked at the plate of food she handed me. I could not read, I could not write; all my powers seemed locked up inside me. At length, exhausted, I dozed in my chair. And the echo of my dream returned to me, fevered and haunting: the white-hot flame searing the length of my body, the glowing coals throbbing like two staring eyes, and the pain—screaming silently, engulfing me—the agony, the heat . . .

I awoke with a start. Karan's eyes were open and he was gazing at me.

"You are a dream," he murmured. "But still, I would have the torment of you rather than nothing at all."

I leaned forward, but was yet fearful of touching him. "I am not a dream," I said. "You are safe in Barrackpore, and I have come to you."

His voice was flat, without strength, without timbre. But a recognition flooded into his eyes that stained them with the purity and peace I remembered.

"Can it truly be so?"

I cried out at the weary sorrow behind his words and, stretching one finger only, touched it cautiously to his parched lips.

"Rest now in peace, for I am here to take care of you."

But his eyes would not leave me, fevered and pale as they were. I called out to Vijaya to bring water and, soaking a cloth in its coolness, bathed his hot face. I smoothed back his hair, usually concealed beneath his wound turban or one of his officer's hats. It was wild black hair, thick and silken against my fingers. He was beginning to look like a man. A hunger for him flared up in me, so that when I touched his smooth skin, I wondered if he could devise what I was thinking and feeling.

I talked to him, I soothed him, I believe I must have sung him to sleep, as I did Winston on nights when he was lonely and restive and his ayah called for me to come to the house. I fell asleep to the sound of my own singing. When I awoke, it was to find myself stretched out on a white cot. Vijaya sat at my feet. As I stumbled up in protest, she hastened to explain.

"Dr. Fielding moved you. He must clean the wound now and examine Karan's injuries. He will call for you soon."

I used the time to bathe in the basin Vijaya provided and change into some of the fresh clothes she had brought from home. "This would be easier—" she began.

"I will not go back there! Constance would see to it that I did not return."

She held her peace then and did her best to assist me. Dr. Fielding had secured a small private room for us, antiseptically clean. We could manage for as long . . . I wondered how long he would keep Karan in this place. If it were true that he was to be moved to Calcutta, I would not be allowed to go with him. Did that mean separation was imminent?

I heard the doctor at the door and pinched my cheeks to give them some color. He came in and nodded to me by way of greeting.

"Your friend fares well this morning. The swelling is subsiding and the wound, though red and irritated, is free of infection." A faint smile touched his features. "Now we must keep it that way."

"How long?"

"Until he is out of danger. A week, perhaps two—" He glanced up at me sharply, realizing where I was taking him. "No, not for your purposes, Lottie." He began shaking his head. "He will need help exercising the atrophied muscles if he hopes to put weight on that leg again and get it to work for him."

"Then he shall be sent to Calcutta?"

"Yes, of a certain he will. And as soon as possible, all things considered."

I sighed and sank into a chair, all my pretense forgotten.

"You have set a hard course for yourself, Lottie, and I admire you." There was more warmth in his voice, despite his professional manner, than I had heard in the major's for a long time. "And in case you are wondering, you *will* prove invaluable to him—give him a reason to live, bring back his will to fight for what's left to him."

"And what might that be?"

"You always entrap me, Lottie. You know my plodding mind can't keep up with your clever one." He leaned over and patted my hand. "Enough to keep living for. And you, my dear, must find a way to convince him of that."

I entered Karan's room feeling unaccountably shy and uncertain. He sat propped up in his bed, cushioned by pillows. He had been washed and groomed and wore a clean white shirt that was open at the throat to reveal his dark, gleaming skin. *White,* I thought to myself, the *color of mourning.*

"Namaste," he greeted me. His voice seemed to have returned to him, and with it that presence I admired and almost resented, because it kept him at a distance from me. "You return, looking as fresh as the morning. Then last night was not a dream."

So this was the tack he was going to take, to preserve his own courage and dignity. Did I possess enough courage to play along?

I smiled brightly. "You look presentable yourself," I replied, but my eyes belied me; my eyes told him so much more. The gash on his cheek, I noted dispassionately, would leave a scar, a long white scar that would increase his aura of masculine mystery.

"What do you think, Charlotte?" he asked in his soft voice.

"I think how handsome you are. I think how much I would like to feel your arms around me and your lips over mine."

He moved, and the pain of it contorted the muscles of his face.

"There! I've spoiled the game already!"

His eyes darkened. A thin layer of perspiration glazed his face. I took up the cloth from the basin, wrung out the excess water, and pressed it gently to his face. "I am sorry for the pain," I said. "But not for anything else. We have no time for this."

"How is it—how is it you come to be here? What price have you paid?"

"One that would have been exacted from me anyway."

He understood. "But more," he persisted. "To walk away would have been easier."

"Love does not walk away."

One of his arms lay over the bedclothes. I saw him clench his long fingers. "How do you know this, my gentle one?"

I placed my hand over the brown one. "I learned it from you."

It was the truth, though it wrenched my whole being to say it. I put my face to his shoulder and rested it lightly there. At length I felt the pressure of his hands on my head, his fingers stroking my hair. The peace of his touch was greater than even the pleasure. I rested a long time, my back arched stiffly to keep from touching his sore, battered body, my face pressed into the warmth of his shoulder, drawing his fragrance and tenderness into my soul.

Chapter Ten

It was not until nightfall that the shadows returned again, dragged back with the darkness. In the hollow, lightless expanse, oppressive thoughts flourish and fears grow out of proportion as though day and hope, once snuffed out, will not again be strong enough to break down this bitter landscape. So both of us felt, Karan especially. He seemed to visibly sink—into the narrow bed, into the narrow oblivion of the moment. *Lame* was a word he had not dared to speak out loud in the bright sunshine. But he said the word now, with half a dozen others that terrified him: cripple, outcast, beggar—a wasted man, a man to be spurned, to be pitied. Each cruel word slashed a wound in my heart. I could not comfort him, divert him, reason with him. When at last he tormented himself into a light, fitful sleep, I sank, exhausted, against my hard chair. But he soon began to mumble and moan, and his breath came in harsh, short rasps—and I realized, with horror, that he was reliving that unearthly scene he had passed through.

A panic rose in me, threatening to choke my breath and my reason. What in heaven's name could I do? Ought I to risk leaving him alone to go in search of the doctor, or anyone who might assist me? I hesitated. Then he reached an arm out, and his fingers closed tightly on my hand.

I gasped. His eyes opened, wide and staring, and they were as wild as his face. His pain must have been terrible; I could feel it in the current that passed from his hand to mine. "Tell me, Karan, tell me what happened!" Even as I pleaded, for his sake, I shrank in weakness and apprehension.

He did tell me, in short, garbled segments, most of what he had suffered. He was at times incoherent, at times terrifyingly lucid. I could see in my mind's eye, so vividly, the great, sharp jaws of the beast—the slow, deadening terror he felt when he realized the hopelessness of his situation—then the magnificent resolve that was somehow able to conquer the power of pain and cold dread, and convince himself that he could achieve the unachievable. How was he able to ignore the screaming demands of his tormented body, and discipline his dark doubts to anticipate victory? I saw it all unfold before me, through both his eyes and mine—suffering through him, and for him. When at last the ordeal shuddered to an end and Karan sank, drained and limp, into a deep sleep, I sat wide-eyed and still, too tired for sleep, too expanded, too drawn out to contain myself. Not many more nights would I spend alone in his company. Though he slept, exhausted and oblivious, his presence was not lost upon me. His spirit, so much more powerful and noble than mine, restored and enhanced all that was good about me. How could I survive without that? How could I go on living and breathing without him?

The darkness of the night around me seemed gentle and harmless compared to the impenetrable darkness that settled with cold portent over my mind.

In the morning came the reckoning Karan exacted of himself. We followed the routine of the previous day, where I was dismissed before his waking and carried out my morning preparations while the doctors and nurses examined and treated the patient, adjusting their recommendations and diagnoses according to what they found. Then I was at last readmitted, and the day began in earnest, as far as we were concerned. I knew that today the first matter would be Karan's apology for what he had put me through. I expected it, but I did not anticipate the direction it would take.

"Come to me," he said as I entered the room and approached his bed. "This must stop. I am wearing you down to a shadow."

"No you are not," I answered. "Despite last night."

He dropped his eyes, studying the weave of the blanket that covered him. "It was cruel and cowardly for me to put you—"

"Nonsense," I interrupted. "I needed to know! I had been given my own foretaste, anyway."

He looked sharply up. "What do you mean?"

I told him about my strange dream and the way it had recurred the first night I sat with him. "Only then did I have a clue to its meaning."

"None of this should be imposed upon you! It is all to no purpose!" He twisted his face into a gruesome expression, which he had hoped would come off as a smile. "I am growing stronger, and am told they will soon move me out of here."

"I know that. I knew from the beginning."

"Exactly, Charlotte." His voice had dropped, become low and serious. I did not like that tone. "You have done more than would ever be required, even hoped for—"

"And you are releasing me now?"

He looked away and nodded his head.

"It is not that simple."

"It *must be that simple.* I cannot bear to punish you further!"

"Every moment I spend with you is blessing, not punishment! You were always the one to remind me of the spiritual bond between us, to convince me of its reality. Do you see, Karan—that is why the dream came? Your sufferings grew so great that they broke through to my spirit, and though I knew not what was happening, I felt your pain."

His face was still turned from me. "Would to heaven it were different." He spoke the words through clenched teeth. I don't believe I was intended to hear them.

"You never felt so before."

"Before!" He spat the word at me, so that I shrank. "In this 'before' you speak of there was a sepoy who loved you, despite

the utter hopelessness of his loving. But he was a man. Perhaps somewhere he cherished the foolish hope of a miracle—a miracle he would have waited a lifetime for. I cannot say."

He moved to face me, and the pain in his eyes was almost too much to bear. "That time is past. It cannot be resurrected. The man who loved you is dead. Mourn him. Hold his memory sacred, if you so desire, within your own heart—"

I cried and reached out, as if to stop him. He imprisoned my arm in a grasp that was bruising.

"*This* changes nothing!" I was breathing heavily, and my head was ringing. "You are what you are, and will always be so. Call yourself dead if the anguish dictates it. We shall be parted—whatever life brings will be dismal following that! It will not be so much easier for me to contrive a life without you simply because I will not carry this one cross with me."

He was watching me, his whole body taut with listening.

"We will not have what we want, but we must contrive to do something fine with what we have—or at some point go mad!"

He drew me close to him. He placed his lips over the ring where it rested against my neck. He kissed my lips, with his warm hands on my hair and my face.

"Forgive me, Charlotte." He murmured the words over and over until the sound of them and the touch of his caresses had cleansed us both.

The following morning Karan was placed in a *bandgari*, or closed carriage, and transferred to the larger medical compound in Calcutta.

"This is good-bye," he had told me.

"But I wish to hear of your progress!"

He shook his head, some of the old patience and gentleness evident. "It will not work, Charlotte. We have been over this." He had smiled wryly. "I *will* progress. That much you may count on."

"But what will you do now? Where will you go?"

"I suspect the doctor will help me find a civilian post in

Bombay or Calcutta. I speak several languages. My mind is quick, and my manners are pleasing." He had shrugged his shoulders, a gesture which made him look boyish and vulnerable. "Where I am is of no consequence. You must come to accept that."

"But not to even know where—"

"Knowing would make no difference. It would not lessen the distance between us, nor soften the pain." He framed my face with his hands. "My heart is yours, my faith, what strength I have . . ." Tears clouded his dark eyes. It is a terrible thing to watch a strong man cry. "All that I am, or may ever with heaven's help become—is *yours,* Charlotte!"

Those were the last words he spoke to me. When they put him on a stretcher and carried him out of the room, I was not there to watch, to wave a pathetic, ineffectual farewell to him. We had planned it that way. I knelt already in the cemetery, where the cool mists of morning still rose from the ground. I knelt beside the silent stone where Roselyn rested, and prayed.

When I returned to the bungalow, it was as if nothing at all had happened. Life went on as before. I asked no questions, and the major volunteered no answers. But "this whole affair," as he called it, sat between the two of us now. I wondered if that distance distressed him, as it did me.

Constance? Constance was a master at ignoring realities and contriving life to her liking. That she was unkind was something she would have given no credence to. Perhaps in her eyes she was doing me a favor to ignore my childish and thoughtless dalliance and, by so doing, readmit me into the grace of her presence, and the grace of society, where she believed I belonged.

There was no grace for me. In my weakness I hungered for it. I moved through my days painfully, methodically, not allowing myself to think beyond the next hour, indeed, beyond the next breath. I attended the Fancy Fair and performed the duties assigned to me. I was dimly aware of many faces turned in my direction, many whispered conversations. They did not seem to concern me at all. These people were strangers. They mattered not in the least to me. I was forced to dwell in this body, in close proximity to them, but such facts were of no consequence. Nothing was of any real consequence anymore.

I was also vaguely aware of Vijaya's concern for me. But a great void separated us, and I could find no way to bridge it. I had been back a few days when I realized that I had not seen Winston since my return. I spoke to her of it.

"He has been waiting for you to summon him," she said.

Then I knew that I had one friend in my suffering. I knew she had been watching out for me with that simple wisdom she had.

Winston was subdued, uncertain in my presence. I had not only stepped out of his life for a season, but I had come back obviously changed. He sensed it with that keen perception children seem to bring with them from a world less obscure and dissembling than this. His wide blue eyes followed my every movement. I could not get him to speak without much cajoling, and then he weighed his words carefully. Therefore I was more than surprised when, the second morning following our resumption of his daily visits, he dropped Mischief's lead and let the monkey run off to his own pursuits, and then fixed his solemn young gaze on me.

"Someone else has died, haven't they?"

His words sent my head reeling. "Why do you say that?"

"I can see in your eyes. It is like when my mother died. You are so sad and lonely, the way I was then."

I stared dumbly at him. But he came up and slipped his small, moist hand into mine. "I'll take care of you. It will get better, Lottie."

"I don't think so," I said, wondering at this unguarded freedom of speech with him.

It was plain that my pain distressed him, but I could not pretend for his sake. Perhaps that was cruel of me, but I felt incapable of it. For the rest of that day, and several days following, he made it his special province to look after me, provide me with treats and flowers, bring our favorite stories for me to read. Such mature concern was uncanny, almost unnatural in a child only four years of age. But the power of his innocence was the only thing stronger than the power of my grief.

A week passed, then another, so it seemed. And then, one evening, Major Hillard arrived at our door. Vijaya showed him into the parlor, where I sat reading. When I looked up and saw him, my amazement must have shown on my face.

"Winston is worried about you," he said bluntly, though trying to lighten the words with a smile. "He says you are not well or happy. I'm not certain what the child means. . . ." He was obviously nervous. "But I thought this might help."

He held out a package to me. When I hesitated he added, "I had occasion to be in Calcutta a week ago, and I picked it up expressly with you in mind."

"Why?" I wanted to ask. I undid the wrappings and drew out one of the loveliest cashmere shawls I had ever set eyes on. I lifted it to my face. "These are very dear."

"I have friends," he said, then added, with obvious emphasis, "Besides, that is of no matter. A gift is a gift."

"I am sorry to be so ungracious a receiver," I replied, feeling sincerely subdued. "I am not accustomed—I am not accustomed to much kindness these past weeks."

There. The words had come out. I had not meant to be so blunt, but I was not sorry for it. Did he know, this man standing before me, of my poor, disgraced station? Most probably so. And yet he trusted his only son to my care and company.

"Miss Simmons, please. Will you drape that shawl around your lovely young shoulders and ride out with me?"

"To what purpose?" I asked.

"The governor-general has just acquired several Himalayan pheasants. They have been brought down to his grounds here in the care of half a dozen of his most trusted gardeners. Come. I should like to see what you think of them."

I acquiesced. I could think of no quick or logical excuse for denying him. His palanquin stood at the gate with two camels harnessed to it. The curtains had been removed so the cool night air could reach us. It smelled of hibiscus and the yellow blooms of the tall amaltash trees, and it smelled of the river water, which ran fresh and sweetly this time of year.

The birds were magnificent. Two dozen or more of them, their bronzed blue coats shimmering like the scales of a mermaid, so startling blue that neither the shades of the sky nor the stains of the ocean could compare with them. The whole of the birds' bodies were blue, save for a bright tuft of green on their heads and a reddish brown dusting along the tips of their tails and wings.

"They are delicate creatures," Major Hillard explained.

"How so?" I asked.

"Apparently they can die, literally, of fright. If not handled properly they will faint away and often die soon afterward."

It can be so with people, I mused to myself. *But in our sophisticated state of advancement we have contrived ways to die on the inside only, so that it need never show—and no company, no army need be robbed of their expenditure in us.*

"An uneasy investment, I should think," I said aloud.

"Worth it for the sake of beauty?" he asked.

"Ideally so," I responded. "But for whose sake? For the sake of possession? I'll warrant you and I shall partake, shall benefit more from this beauty, as you call it, than will the governor-general and all of his officers together. So, in a most vital way we possess his acquisitions more surely, more lastingly than he ever shall."

He liked me; he liked my spunk and spirit, my habit of clear thinking. But his liking did not annoy me as it had in the past. I was not performing for his sake, nor displaying my cleverness in order to lighten his mood. Let him think what he pleased; it was of no consequence whatever to me.

I slept well that night. Perhaps the effects of the fresh air. I awoke feeling rested, with a sense—however thin and fragile—of well-being. Before I was properly dressed, Vijaya came in to say that Dr. Fielding was waiting in the small breakfast room, or morning room, for me. I hastened my preparations and arrived a bit dewy and breathless to find him savoring his second cup of Gopal's coffee and enjoying his peace.

My eyes asked the question I was afraid to speak out loud. "Come with me into the gardens," he said.

The moment we were deep into the foliage and out of earshot he put his hands on my arms. "I may be damned for doing this, but I have come to tell you that your young man is well. He has pushed his muscles to do incredible things for him—"

"Of course," I said, feeling a bit light-headed.

"He will walk. I can assure you of that. And the chances are good that I can find a post for him as both teacher and interpreter at the academy in Calcutta."

I nodded and squeezed his hand in gratitude. "God bless you," I said.

It was enough. Karan was well. He was still close to me, and might very well remain so. Yet the mere mention of his name crumbled all my careful defenses. I longed for the touch of his hands, the sound of his voice washing over me, like the clear light of heaven. Would I ever know such joys again?

When Winston found me later that morning, I was morose, even taciturn. There was no light left in my countenance, no sign of hope. He understood that. He slipped his small hand into mine and sat down beside me, never saying a word. His presence sanctified my grief somehow, and lent me the strength to keep breathing from moment to moment, despite the despair.

Chapter Eleven

The sticky heat of April was upon us, as well as the fleas and mosquitoes that torment to distraction. The tatties came out, and the big, creaking punkahs to play their tedious rhythm through our days and our nights. Constance was in a state, trying to decide if she ought to take Lucy to the mountains or remain here, free from the hazards and fatigues of such a long journey. There were certainly arguments to be made for both plans. But to stay at the post during the months of intense heat would require the most steady of nerves. I was led to believe I could do as I liked, stay with Constance or travel with one of the other families to Simla; neither appealed to me in the least. I did not see the shadow that was stretching its wide wings above me, preparing to fall.

The weekly dances seemed to grow more frenzied than usual, laced with the excitement of change. Many of the women would be leaving their husbands behind at their posts, to labor the tedious months away. So the subtle flirtations began, some of which would bloom into alarming proportions once Simla was reached. The young officers, bored and without attachments, encouraged such behavior from wives as bored as themselves, women often married to men much older than they were, men whose youthful passions had been wrung dry by the hot Indian sun. Of course, there were also those men who preferred native consorts. As observer I could not help wondering how many happy and harmonious marriages there were. Was I a fool even to wonder? Did such a thing as a happy marriage, by a young girl's romantic ideas, even exist? I knew Constance and the major had less than an ideal union; but I also knew he was faithful to her. And I was certain he had experienced as many opportunities to fall from grace as had the next man, probably more. He was attractive in a sincere, forthright way which was enhanced by the appeal of his thick, graying hair and the air of quiet power about him. What of the dashing red-haired captain, Frances Simmons, and the native girl, Sita? What had it been like for them? I believed each of my parents must have sacrificed much for the other. And certainly that implied something, something rare and out of the ordinary.

The mood of the camp had its effect upon Major Hillard. He sought my company openly now and bestowed obvious attentions upon me, regardless of place or circumstances. Most of the times I resigned myself to this, as a minor unpleasantness which must be endured. At times, if I were honest with myself, I enjoyed his keen conversations, his quick perceptions, or merely the simple fact of having someone to be with, someone who obviously admired me and was anxious to please. At times when he crowded me or pushed his advantage, I would strike out at him like a cornered viper; then he would move back, go more slowly, be more cautious of me.

I am not certain why I continued to go out at all, save for the general boredom of my life and that restlessness of youth which can prove such a tormenting affliction. One evening in early April, however, I was suffering from a nasty headache which I was certain the high, whining wind would show no pity to, so I declined going out. Oddly enough, the major had at last cajoled Constance into accompanying him, using as part of his argument the fact that I would be present in the house to assist Radha in the care of the child. She went unwillingly; she had lost her taste for society. She had lost the savor of all things, in my opinion, which included even the ability to enjoy the baby girl she adored. But I was glad, I must admit, to be rid of her and have the house to myself.

The evening progressed with a light and slow deliciousness. Radha and I played with Lucinda Jane, who was as mild and sweet as a lamb and went to sleep as soon as we put her down, with no bother at all. I had just situated myself on the most comfortable divan in the sitting room, with a tray of fruit at my elbow and a book in my lap, when Vijaya entered the room, a small native boy crowding her elbow, looking out with wide eyes.

"Baby of Memsahib Abbot very ill and screaming. Ayah cannot stop her. Come quickly, she says. Please."

I threw a shawl around my shoulders and walked out into the night. The wind had risen; I thought there was an evil sound to it—a sorrowing wind. I bent my head against the blinding swirls of dust, the fine grit that caught in my teeth, scratched my skin, and stung my eyes. I began to run; it was quicker to go the short distance between the two bungalows on foot than to take precious time to arrange some form of transport. I arrived at the low door breathless, with Vijaya still several yards behind. Dust filled my lungs; I shook it from my skirts as I entered, anxious as to what I would find.

The small boy led me back to where my own ears would have taken me. I thought idly, as I passed through the rooms, how like the blonde, pretty young Gwen Abbott they were. The nursery was so brightly lit that I had to squint my eyes at first, just in order to see. A very young looking ayah was walking the length of the small room, cradling a child in her arms, patting the little arched back and pressing the screaming infant to her. When she saw me a string of anguished explanations broke from her, but in such rapid and garbled Hindustani that I could scarcely catch one word in three.

"Give her to me," I said, extending my arms. The child was in obvious pain. The fine, delicate features of her face were contorted awfully, and the piercing cries that shook her small frame sent a chill of cold terror along my spine.

"How long?" I demanded in Hindustani. "How long has she been thus?"

"Very long time," the girl replied, her eyes wide and

frightened. "Two, three hours. I try to feed her, she will not stop crying. I lay her in bed, she screams all the louder. I walk the room—" She raised her thin arms in appeal, feeling sorry for herself and hoping for a bit of sympathy.

"*Bas!*" I said sharply. "I am worried about this child."

The baby's cries had grown weak; her skin looked pale and pinched. I laid her gently on the bed—she shuddered, and her whole little body went taut. What was wrong? Had she twisted and broken a limb, swallowed something that was eating her insides up? She was soaked in perspiration, even her crumpled clothes damp with it. I lifted her gown and began to draw the folds up, hoping a careful examination might show me something, or at least provide me with clues.

I gasped and let the soft fabric fall from my fingers as I took a few involuntary steps back. Out from a crease of the white dress, across the tender, tightened chest crawled a scorpion, the dark, repulsive body moving above its thin, tentacled legs with nauseating deliberation. I put my hand to my mouth, then gasped again as I heard a movement behind me, and Vijaya brushed past in one swift movement, slamming a hard object against the creature, cracking its back, crushing its insidious power to destroy. I drew the suffering infant into my arms, crying to the ayah as I did so. "Send someone immediately to fetch this child's parents! And the doctor, Dr. Fielding—he must come at once!"

My hands trembled as I began to uncover the poor little body and realized how many stings there were. The wretched servant girl! How ignorant and untrained was she? Unwittingly, each time she hugged the child to her she angered or annoyed the insect, who, in his fear and instinct, struck again and again. If only—!

I bathed the small trembling body in warm ammonia water, crooning soothingly under my breath. The cries had grown feeble now. The blue eyes looked vacant, empty of comprehension. I shuddered. I had never before felt quite so helpless. Something must be done! Dr. Fielding must find a way to save this beautiful and innocent child!

The parents arrived first. Ethan Abbot was a slender, nondescript sort of man, very proper in conduct and manner. But he looked wild and disheveled now. Gwen Abbott's heart-shaped face, with its fair skin and bridge of freckles across the nose, made her appear little more than a child herself. Where was Dr. Fielding? Inwardly cursing his absence, I tried to explain to the stricken parents what had happened. They stared at me, horrified, uncomprehending. Such things did not really happen, did they? Especially not to a tiny first child, delicate, porcelain-fine, with eyes as blue as the morning? Their eyes were hungry with the need for me to tell them that this horror was simply not true.

The young mother came to stand beside me. She bent over her infant as though she were afraid to touch her. Then she reached out a tentative hand and began to smooth the pale curve of cheek with her fingers. I looked away. Then I stepped back and let the father slip up beside her. I felt Vijaya come up behind me and give a tug to my hand.

"You have done all you can do here. Dr. Fielding stands at the door. You must come home with me."

I stared at her blankly. I felt Dr. Fielding's firm, lean hands close over my shoulders, but only a quick squeeze in passing.

"How do you manage to get yourself mixed up with all the misery in Barrackpore, young lady?" he scolded. "You scoot on home. I'll take care of things here."

His expression was grim. As I stumbled after Vijaya I couldn't get his image out of my mind. *Better his face,* I thought as I stretched across my bed, *than the tortured face of the baby.* I would not agree to undress. I let Vijaya cover me with a blanket, but I left instructions that she was to wake me as soon as she learned anything of the fate of the child.

I don't know how long I slept, fitfully and lightly, hearing Constance and the major's entrance, aware of shuffling footsteps and muffled voices, and all the annoying night sounds that inhabit a house. Vijaya awoke me about an hour before dawn, when night still held the world in its grip.

"The child—she died peacefully, in her mother's arms. No more crying, no pain."

I wanted to scream; I needed to scream. I ran out into the

garden, which was only a mass of shadows and cold shapes. I ran as far from the house as I could. Then, burying my face against the twisting trunks of the banyan, I let myself cry—cry out all the anger and confusion, all the misery and helplessness that had poisoned my system. But the terrible sobbing did not grant me relief. At length I arose, feeling bleak and drained.

"What is the purpose?" I asked the emptiness around me. "What does God hope to achieve by means of man's terrible suffering? Are some few, the blessed, the lucky, redeemed? Are there others of us who are doomed to live in the grip of the darkness for the rest of our lives?"

The young mother, bereft of her child, was not the only one suffering that night. Apparently Constance, when she arrived home and learned what had happened, went into a state of panic, illogical but nonetheless terrifying. What had happened to the Abbot baby was just what Constance had always feared. This was positive proof that she had not been an alarmist, a prey to unreasonable fears. When I arose in the morning, it was late and the household unusually quiet. Constance was waiting for me when I walked into the dining room.

"The baby is dead," she said.

"I know. Vijaya told me."

"You were there, Lottie! You saw her only moments before!"

"I do not wish to talk about it, Constance!"

She went on, as though I had not spoken. "It could have been Lucy."

"It could not have been Lucy! No one here is that careless. It was a freakish thing, Constance." I laid my hand on her arm. "It would not happen again in a hundred years—"

She shook her arm free. "Choose to ignore it, if that lessens your sense of responsibility. I know this was a warning, I know what is expected of me!"

"Nonsense," I responded without thinking. Her head snapped up, and from the look in her eye I thought she might very well strike me. But she turned, in a swishing of wide, starched skirts, and walked out of the room.

I stared after her. Whatever was happening inside Constance was real, and should not be ignored. I sent word for Cinnamon to be saddled, while I bolted down some fruit and warm wheat bread. The hour for the morning promenade had long since passed. If I were lucky, I might still find the major at the officer's mess enjoying the last of his coffee before the drilling of troops began.

Cinnamon was frisky, wanting to stretch his legs, protesting the tight rein I kept on him. "I know how it is, old boy," I murmured, for I had been on a tight rein myself ever since my eighteenth birthday six months before. Crisis following crisis seemed only to shrink the circumference allotted me, and I felt the sharp control keenly.

I turned in at the club, handed Cinnamon over to a boy, and cleared the steps in no time. "Major Reid," I called out as heads turned at the sight of a woman in these sacrosanct chambers.

"In the billiards room," someone shouted, "third on the left."

I nodded and headed in that direction. The major met me at the door; I was not to be vouchsafed even a glimpse of the room's interior. "Is this important, Charlotte?" he demanded, meaning, *It had better be*. The coldness in his voice, so customary now, nevertheless sent a chill down my spine.

"It is Constance. She is—not herself. I think you had better talk to her."

"It is this confounded affair with the Abbott's baby, isn't it?"

I nodded.

"Gives me the creeps, Lottie." He shook his head sadly. "I can't seem to get through to her nowadays. And frankly, it worries me."

That he would state his concern so bluntly seemed to give life and possibility to all the vague evils that threatened us.

We were nearing the entrance to the building again. "I will meet you at home," he instructed with a curt nod.

I rode Cinnamon back at a more leisurely pace, though he still pranced in hopes of something better. When I entered the bungalow, Constance was gone.

I called out to her. I questioned the butler, the cook, and the hamal, or housekeeper, who sat tediously dusting the mistress's tall shelf of what-nots. Rosina was missing, too. But Lucy remained with Radha, her ayah. Poor Radha knew nothing at all.

"Memsahib say she has ordered carriage and is going out. The child is in my safekeeping. If any harm comes to her—I am to pay with my life."

"She was distraught," I tried to explain. "It will be all right, Radha." I comforted her and planted a kiss on Lucinda Jane's cheek.

I shook my head at the major as he entered the room. "Do you have any idea where she might be?"

"Not I!" he blustered, arching his black brow in affront, obviously implying that women's daily schedules were most certainly beneath his notice. But he did not detect the bitter edge to my smile. I knew very well the particulars of his routine, which was no more rigorous nor impressive than that assigned to the women. He rose at four-thirty each morning, parading with his men for at least an hour, while there was yet a breath of cool air to breathe. Then it was off to the officers' mess for coffee before returning for a leisurely bath. Perhaps after that he would conduct a private drill or inspection, or find some suitable occupation at his desk which would fill the hours till *tiffin,* the Anglo-Indian word for the midday meal which is served precisely at 2:00. By half past five he and his fellow officers could most often be found relaxing in the parks and gardens before dining two hours later, which meal would be followed by cards or billiards, or even dancing, depending upon the occasion or the night of the week.

Most officers felt rather used up by ten o'clock, which was considered lights out for the station, though that strict expectation did not always apply to the married man. Not much of consequence occurred on a day-to-day basis; indeed, I often thought that the ladies accomplished more real reform and occasioned more progress, weak and ineffectual as they were in this climate, and sandwiched between the male social structure of their husbands and that of the many and varied Indian castes.

The major was disturbed. He did not do well with waiting, yet was too sincerely upset to return without some news of Constance. As he paced the veranda, her palanquin arrived in front of the bungalow, the coolies staggering under the weight and the fast pace she had set them. The major worked to contain himself; it would never do to display distress in front of the servants. By the time he got Constance alone in his office with the door closed, his impatience was irritating him as much as summer fleas irritate the hide of a monkey.

What he intended to say I could easily guess. But I do not believe he was given much opportunity. Constance spoke first, and what she said blanched his skin and rendered him speechless. He called me into the room after only a few moments.

"Constance has made a decision," he informed me, "and she will not listen to me. Talk her out of it, please."

Please. Even then, despite both curiosity and compassion, I wanted to say: *How dare you ask favors at my hand!*

"What is it, Constance?"

"I am taking Lucinda Jane and returning to England."

She had done it; she had astounded the both of us.

"I have already sent off word to my sister. She will take both of us in."

"Both of you?" I queried. "What of the major and me?"

She waved our concerns away with a little flutter of her hand. "The major has his work, and you . . ." She paused. A look entered her eye that had some meaning to it which I could not discern.

"This is your home. You are the major's wife and he has need of you." I kept my voice at a low and reasonable pitch. "Besides, there are definite hazards to sea travel. Who would accompany you?"

"I have made my arrangements."

"Which are?" the major bellowed.

"You will not dissuade me, Ralph," she crooned, "no matter how loud you shout."

"Will you take Radha?" I asked, trying a different tack.

"I shall secure an English nurse when I arrive. Radha will have to stay here. Only myself, Beth Martin, and her daughter, Ella, will be going."

"And have those arrangements been made?"

She nodded smugly.

"They can be *unmade*." I thought the major looked ill. I could feel my temper beginning to rise in hot prickles along the back of my neck.

"They *could be,*" she intoned slowly. "But I must do this! I must protect my baby. It is the only path left to me."

I opened my mouth to protest, but fear cannot be dissuaded by reason. I glanced at the major's white face.

"I need to return now," he said, as though taking the same cue. "Further discussion will have to wait till tonight."

"That is fine," Constance said, almost breezily. "But nothing will have changed by then, Ralph."

At that word he turned and left her. I felt sickened inside. She did not call me back, she did not protest or entreat; it was as though she were no longer quite with us, as though she had taken a step that removed her from us in some literal way.

For the remainder of the day I avoided her. When evening came and the major had not yet made an appearance, I ordered Cinnamon saddled and rode out into the mall. Cool breezes drifted up from the river, but the air still smelled of dust to me. The band was playing, but the creak and rattle of carriages, the pockets of laughter and conversation fairly well drowned out the sound. I tied my horse to a post and began walking, veering at an angle from the main path. There was nowhere to go. All the places of beauty had become closed and forbidden. Memory stirred, even here.

"Too noisy for thought—or even for real communion, isn't it?"

I jumped at the sound of the voice.

"So sorry. I did not mean to startle you. Miss Simmons, are you quite well?"

"Quite, Major Hillard." Not time yet to air our latest disaster. I was not a teller of tales.

"You look a bit pale. Or is that a terrible thing to say to a lovely young lady?"

He had trouble with the banter of light conversation; but then, so did I.

"You do not offend me," I assured him. "Nor do I consider myself a lovely young lady." I smiled, though I do not enjoy smiling on cue, with no purpose at all. "How fare the Himalayan pheasants?"

"I know no better than you. There is no impetus to see them without your company."

My smile wilted; I gave him no response beyond that, and a silence fell between us. "I suppose I am a bit tired today," I offered at length.

"And a bit bored," he added. "I do not blame you a bit. There is no scope here for a mind and spirit of your caliber."

"But I do not mind it," I said. "And yet your wife, constituted so differently, was most miserable."

I surprised myself with my unkind words. Was I taking my ire out on him?

"Following that theory, you would make do wherever you might happen to be," he said, "and that is an admirable quality."

"I am sorry." I put my hand on his arm. "In truth, there is a trouble which bothers me. But that does not excuse me for speaking so thoughtlessly—"

He placed his hand over mine. It was neither warm nor cold. But I could feel his warmth assail me, frail though it might be.

"Miss Simmons—Charlotte—you could never offend me. My life has been a difficult one for many years—even before Judith died." He pressed my hand with his gloved one. "Your friendship is a breath of fresh air blowing through it—you have renewed my spirit."

I hazarded a glance at his face. His long mustache hid the softness of his mouth so that the expression of his features was partly obscured. His hair, though a thin brown, curled around his temples and his fine, broad forehead. His eyes, deeply set, had a piercing quality to them from which I naturally shrank. I did so now, but with pressure on my hand he detained me.

"Miss Simmons, please. At least a degree of natural sympathy exists between us, I know that it does! Do not deny me—even that."

What was he saying? What did he want? I refused to answer the questions, which were both tiresome and disturbing. I was weary of conflicts and uncertainties. I was weary of Constance's thoughtlessness and the major's coldness. A sympathetic companionship, albeit mundane, had its appeal.

He took my hand and slipped it through the arm it had rested upon and led me away from the others, and I did not resist. I had no heart to. I took every scrap of loveliness or enjoyment the evening offered, snatching at it greedily. I stayed away a long time, luxuriating in the temporary escape Major Hillard had offered me.

It was only when I found myself back in my room, alone, with the door shut tight, that I gave way to tears. They spilled out, as the flecks of silver starlight that patterned my floor, flickering, insubstantial, and comfortless.

Chapter Twelve

Constance stood firm. The days drooped with the heat, the mangoes and sugar melons grew sweeter, the scent of the jasmine as heavy with sweetness as the ripe, fleshy fruits. The punkahs plied day and night, operated by tireless *punkah-wallahs,* whose only job was to keep the big cloth fans continually moving to stir the stale air. Winston and I spent less and less time in the gardens where the mosquitoes were merciless. Inside the house the small green lizards, hunting insects and chasing one another through cracks in the high walls, plopped down at our feet, surprised and stunned for a moment, but soon wiggling and sliding away, only to begin the whole process again.

"India—" I said to Constance one morning as we sat over our *chhoti hazari,* or little breakfast of toast and tea, "India has its compensations, and it has been home to you for a very long time. Will you not miss it?" I felt as though I were playing along with the imaginary schemes of a very naughty and willful child.

"I do not believe so."

"Much that you love will remain here."

She looked up at me sharply. "Ralph will follow in time. Which brings me to something I have been meaning to discuss with you." With long, nervous fingers she folded her napkin in her lap. "It will be impossible for you to remain in this household once I am gone."

I must have blinked stupidly at her. I felt entirely stunned.

"You must see how it would be. Without me here you would be looked upon as another woman, living with a married man, free of all constraint or supervision—"

"Living with a married man whose wife has deserted him!" I blurted. "For goodness sake, Constance, I am his daughter!"

Her eyes, neither brown nor gray, watched me as if from a distance, detached and appraising. "Indeed you are not. Not by blood. And that makes all the difference."

"Does it?" I asked, my voice sounding hollow in my ears.

"You are a grown woman now. All the implications must be apparent to you."

I said nothing. I was painfully aware that Constance had not invited me to accompany her to England. To be fair, it might in part be simply the legitimate reality of finances. The journey was a long and costly one. Men with large families often depleted their means or nearly beggared themselves sending their sons back to school. It was a vicious circle: a man needed money to purchase a higher rank, and therefore higher pay and privilege, in order to afford a decent standard of living. Yet when all his means went in that direction, the increase in salary did not compensate sufficiently to subsidize the terrible cost of travel and education.

Yet it *was* more than that. She had expressed no concern, no regrets at the prospect of parting. She had shut both the major and myself out from her consciousness. And now this.

"You need to get on with your own life, anyway—it is time for that, Lottie," she was saying. "And there are prospects, you know."

"Prospects?" The word sent a shudder through me. I struggled to keep my face passive. I *would* remain calm in her presence!

"You are a lovely girl, spirited and intelligent. Most men would find you excellent marriage material." She smiled, her mouth forming a thin, mirthless slash across the narrow length of her face. "One I know in particular."

"I shall make my own choice when the time comes." My heart felt tight and constricted; I could almost feel it beating.

"Nonsense! It is not done that way, Charlotte—one selects where one can."

I knew what she was saying. Her eyes were filled with the meaning she did not quite dare put into words.

"You are telling me I have no right to determine even the most vital aspects of my own life!"

"Who of us does? You are beginning to grow up, Charlotte, if you recognize that."

I stood, pushing my chair back with such force that it clattered backward. I could hear the soft pattering of half a dozen pairs of servants' feet approaching the closed door, hovering, waiting, not certain what they should do.

"Running off in a temper won't solve anything, Lottie. You must think about what I have said and come to terms with it." She jutted her narrow chin out in emphasis and checked the ivory watch she wore at her waist. "Will you be a dear and tell Radha to bring Lucy in to me now?"

"Certainly, Constance."

Somehow I cleared the space between us and made it through the door and away from her. I felt that I was going to be sick. I sought refuge in the farthest spot of the garden, and even Vijaya had the grace and sense not to follow me. I sat alone beneath the hot shadow of the banyan for a very long time. I did not have to think; realization came stronger than thought, and I knew in my heart there was no escape.

The hours of the day were like small, scalding stones that burned into my heart, one by one. The major took his evening meal with friends and stayed on for a game of cards. Constance retired at nine-thirty, and the major walked in the door at quarter past eleven.

I was waiting for him, standing in the hall with my candle in hand when he opened the door.

"What the deuce, Charlotte! You gave me an awful fright! Has something happened?"

"I need to speak with you. Now."

"Must we, my dear? It is terribly late—" He took a look at my face and nodded. "Very well, then. Hold that light up and follow me."

Once in his office he settled heavily into the padded chair that sat by his desk. In the dim, silent house, with no one else stirring, I felt suddenly ill at ease. This was an awkward subject I was approaching, anyway.

"I talked with Constance today," I began, "or rather, I listened while she informed me of the new conditions she is setting. Is this all her idea—or are these your terms as well, sir?"

The major sighed. His graying hair glistened in the yellow glow of the candle. He leaned over and lit one of the swinging oil lamps. *He is playing for time,* I thought, folding my hands in my lap.

"She's entrapped us all, as well you know, Lottie. But I dare say her conclusions are right."

"You agree, then, that it would be unseemly for me to live here alone with you?" I knew the presence of two dozen servants in the house counted as nothing. They were nonhuman for all practical purposes, and certainly without influence in the moral and social occurrences which took place around them. We lived by the strict British order of things, and nothing else mattered at all.

"I fear so," the major replied, coughing into his hand, then fussing with his collar.

"So. She is to have her way in all things. You are to have neither wife nor household—will you move in with the bachelors, find a niche somewhere in their quarters?" I did not wait for a reply. "And with me it is worse. I have no home and no future. You have already seen to that. She is merely putting on the finishing touches."

"Now, see here, Lottie." The major was immediate bristles. He knew he could not defend Constance, but he would certainly try the job for himself. "It was providence. You would have no life with that sepoy, even if you refuse to admit it. Did you ever think that his accident was a turn of good luck for you?"

I do not believe I had ever, up to that point in my life, had the urge to strike a man, but I trembled with that passion now. The helplessness of my situation washed over me, threatened to suffocate me.

"I am sorry, sir, to have inconvenienced you at this late hour. I think I shall go to my room now." I clasped my candle in trembling hands, keeping my face averted, praying that my pain did not show. He let me go; he was only too happy to do so. I walked the length of the hall, the wavering shadows the candle threw mocking me, reminding me cruelly that my life was only a shadow, a one-dimensional image with no substance to it at all. I entered the room that contained all my intimate possessions—treasures dating back to my childhood—all that I really held dear. In the pale half-light they appeared gray and unappealing. I thought, as I crawled into my cold bed, *There is no longer anything of me here.* I felt it—as though something within me had involuntarily recoiled and retreated. It terrified me. I had nowhere to go. No one to turn to. I lay awake all night, staring at the dingy white ceiling. Under cover of darkness I could admit what seemed too harsh for the daylight—I could face the cruel fact that, even if I followed the mad, romantic notions of girlhood and ran after Karan and threw myself at his feet—even then, he would never accept me. He believed in his heart that I was too good for him. No, it was not that. He believed that he could never provide me with the kind of life I deserved. He accepted the fact that we were both victims, both crushed in the British system, from which there was no escape. He refused to further cripple my life by imposing his desires upon me, when they were not for my good. *My good!* Dear heaven! Why had all men the right to determine my good but me?

The morning, gray and seedy, colored the patch of window and outlined the shapes in my room. It was the same. I had become a stranger. I rose and prepared myself for the day, dressing in an old, plain-colored frock and sturdy shoes. I did not go into the morning meal, but instructed Vijaya to gather fruits and breads and a large vial of water for me. With these and a satchel filled with books and drawing papers I slipped out to the stables and waited while Cinnamon was saddled, wondering for the first time as I ran my hand along the smooth curve of his back what would happen to him.

I passed the day in hiding, I suppose you could call it, spending some time in the gardens, some time down by the river, some at a small pond past the row of bachelor's chummeries which Karan and I had found. I knew my behavior was considered highly irregular in a society where females did not go out unless accompanied by at least an ayah, and in most cases a male bodyguard. But I had grown up here and maintained some of the wild freedom of childhood, extended by the fact that I had the big red horse to escort me.

I read my favorite poems, and I sketched the places that were dear to me, feeling a vague need to do so. It seemed everyone in India sketched, and I was as skilled at it as the next person, though not blessed with particular talent. Yet I derived some peace, if not pleasure, from the exercise.

Though I kept to the shady spots, the heat of the day was oppressive. I found myself back at the park where lines and clusters of large trees afforded a coolness found nowhere else. *It will come,* I told myself, *and soon. And I must be ready.* The day had provided nothing new, nothing more illuminating than had been revealed through the night. My pride prevented me from appealing, in dishonor and destitution, to any of the other families at the station. In truth, I knew none of them well. Constance might call me a young woman, but I had lived as a daughter of the household, jealously guarding the last wisps of childhood and considering the adults around me, in a detached and disinterested light, as my parents' friends. Nor had I any desire to go to England, if such a course were open to me. I could not conceive of a home other than India. To talk of crossing the great ocean and going to a place as far away and foreign sounding as England—though I knew that others did it—seemed preposterous to me. What I possessed of my parents resided in the discords and harmonies of the life around me. What was left of Karan—No! To be separated from him by a waste of ocean more terrifying than any desert—no, that could not be!

Karma had been unkind to me; perhaps I had earned such trials in a state of life before this. Was such suffering for my eventual good and salvation, as the Christians would teach? I did not know, and I did not much care. I longed for the tenderness and wisdom of the mother I had never known. I longed for the strength and protection of the man I loved; both were denied. I had no choice but to go on, and to pray for the strength to do so.

As though I myself had willed it, I looked through the late afternoon haze to see Major Hillard walking toward me. It was not in the least unusual that he should be in the park at this hour, and just as natural that he should recognize Cinnamon and seek me out. Yet I knew, I knew what he was doing here, and what he would say. He seemed to approach in slow motion. I could see the sun glinting off the buttons of his uniform, and his hair, the pale shades and consistency of fine moss, curling in wet tendrils across his forehead. In the space between his eyebrows a thin white scar was sketched; the odd line lent him some grace. *He cannot be much younger than my own father would have been,* I thought with a sudden jolt. But then, I knew that. I had just never thought of it in the terms I was now forced into thinking of. He lifted his eyes. I met his gaze with no resistance, and yet with no promise.

"Charlotte! We are well met." He tipped his hat to me, the well-bred gentleman. *He has already spoken to Major Reid,* I realized. *This has already been settled without me.*

"Although what I have to say is of a delicate nature, I would rather speak in the freedom of this setting than . . ." He paused, realizing he had worked himself into a bit of a corner.

"Yes, rather than in the confinement of Constance's home." I spoke the words for him. "I appreciate your thoughtfulness, and I hope my candidness will not offend you. I know no other way." *It is vital,* I thought, *if what you are going to ask me transpires.*

He nodded in tacit agreement.

"It would be vain and unkind for me to pretend ignorance of your situation, my dear, and the distress you must be suffering."

"Is that why you came?"

"I would have approached you regardless. I have grown very fond of you, Charlotte."

He was already using my name, in anticipation.

"I know my request is presumptuous—I do not feel worthy of you—yet you would do me the greatest honor if you would agree to become my wife."

They were pretty words; I knew they were little more than pretty words to him. Yet they had the power to send a warmth stirring through me, and I saw that there were tears in his eyes.

"Do you love me, Major Hillard?"

"I am not the most emotional of men, Charlotte." He lifted my hand and seemed to almost cradle it within his own. "But I can tell you honestly—though it is a sad admission—that I feel more genuine regard for you and tenderness toward you than I have ever before felt for a woman."

Quite an admission, indeed, considering that he had already had two other wives. Conveniently, neither was here to defend herself, nor to confirm his sorry claims.

"Then you have not known much happiness in your life."

"I have known as much as most men know." My bluntness was not disarming him. "You are an unusual girl, Charlotte—you fascinate me! No woman has ever had that effect upon me before."

Did the women you were married to know as much happiness as most women know? I wanted to ask. He was a bright man, and a capable one. But on this level of life—the nurturing, the intimate . . .

"I do not love you," I said. I did not say to him, *I love another.* No man who goes by the name can bear to hear such words spoken. I could spoil any chance of trust, of happiness between us. And, worse, I would betray the purity of that love by revealing it to this ordinary, if well-intentioned man.

"Love will come," he assured me.

"You appear confident of that. Can love be so ordered, so controlled by the commonest dictates?"

"In time you will see," he replied, stroking the hand he held. "I mean to take care of you. I shall try to make you happy.

Will you marry me, Charlotte?"

I looked down at the tips of my shoes, half-hidden by the matted, sweet-smelling grasses through which a thin lizard darted. "You are certain you truly wish this union, despite all I have just said to you?" I thought it only fair to give the man one more chance.

"I do," he replied, and I could feel a sudden fervor in his voice and the touch of his hand.

"You trust I can make you happy . . ." I left the word trailing. I did not add, *despite all you know that stands between us, which has not been said.*

"I have no concerns on that account," he responded. "Will you be my wife, Charlotte Simmons?"

"I will," I said.

"I am the happiest of men," he murmured, and pressed his lips to my hand. Then, to my utter consternation, he lowered his face and pressed his lips over mine. The touch was not unpleasant. But it sent a jolt of pain through me. The final step had been taken—the final betrayal been made. There was no going back, no reclaiming what had been lost. My only consolation lay in the fact that the woman who would become Mrs. Hillard was not the same woman who mourned her lost sweetheart, who mourned a life forever lost to her. The woman who would become Mrs. Hillard was a stranger to me.

Chapter Thirteen

We were married quietly. He was, after all, a recent widower, and I had no desire for the insincere fanfare of which Constance was capable. The most difficult thing for me—being still young and a creature of pride—was allowing Constance and the major to believe they had "won," that they were having their way. I appeared docile and resigned and obedient; but this was not so. I felt my spirit had ascended to a higher plane of existence: I would do what was required of me with dignity, not allowing them the final victory of seeing my disappointment, my anguish and pain.

Perhaps the only person altogether happy on the occasion was my new little son. Winston could not get over the prize life had handed him. *At least he knows my worth,* I would think, watching his solemn but happy face.

The major had been generous. As he was breaking up house himself, it was agreed that I should have both Vijaya and Radha, as well as Gopal, who was one of the best cooks in India, and even Domingo, his steward, if I liked. What was more, he would pay the next half-year's wages, as a wedding gift to the both of us. And he made it clear that Cinnamon was to go along with me, as well as any personal possessions I wished to take from the house. I disliked admitting to his generosity, being beholden to him. But nothing short of a narrow and niggardly behavior could prevent it, and I would not stoop to that. I knew the major was, in part, salving his conscience. This new, self-contained Constance had no qualms at all. Her mind was elsewhere.

It was I who saw to the details, arranging a seamstress to help create the modest trousseau I was preparing. Vijaya and I arranged for the food and the flowers, the transfer of goods and servants. It was a very sad thing to watch the breaking up of a household, to tell the stricken wallahs that they must seek work elsewhere. Major Hillard had a staff of his own, of course, and I did not wish to disfranchise any of them. But at the same time, I wanted my own people around me, scant remains, as they were, of a life that was past. Since I would be married and sleeping with a husband, I made arrangements for Vijaya and her husband to have one of the servant's rooms in Major Hillard's house. Her husband worked in one of the nearby bungalows, but I wanted her close to me, as she always had been. How strange, that I had given her private life almost no thought before this time. She was not in the habit of spending her nights with her husband, not on a regular basis. Who did we think we were, that we could behave as though we owned these people, and expect them not to protest?

The monkey, Mischief, was coming—more was the pity—to be Winston's pet now, and Soobratta, the monkey boy, with him. As far as I was concerned, we could cut down the servants from both households and I would be happy. The thought of suddenly becoming the memsahib, in charge of the house, settling the countless domestic disputes and keeping everyone happy and dealing honorably with one another, seemed overwhelming to me. Nor was I overpleased at taking up quarters in another woman's household, with her shade always going before me. Yet I did not wish to pursue the major's suggestion of simply switching bungalows. To live here with Constance's shadow hovering over me seemed intensely undesirable.

When it came down to the day, to the very last breathless moments of my own solitary life—hovering on the thin, insubstantial edge of two worlds—then my heart cried out for a mother's arms around me, for her reassuring voice to guide me through the dangerous narrows ahead. I walked alone. The only voice I heard was the one I carried inside my heart. *Spirit can be passed on,* it said. *Your mother's spirit is strong in you, part of what renders you like no other.* Karan's words were my only comfort. And yet—and yet—when I lay in bed that night beside a stranger, when he gathered me into his arms, my spirit mourned for the kind of union my mother must have known. She had gone willingly into the arms of a man who adored her, who had awakened her love as the gentle spring sunlight awakens a delicate flower. I grieved for her happiness, lost so early, and I grieved for my own, which was not to be. And I closed my eyes and pretended that Karan was bending above me, encircling me in an embrace that nothing on this earth could break.

I had been two weeks in my new home, as a wife and mother, when Constance left on the ship. I did not go to the wharves to see her off; there was no reason I should. Little of pretense was left between us. Yet—how strange people are! When I went to the bungalow—whose rooms already seemed to echo of the emptiness that was upon them—she clung to me in tears. I could see fear in her eyes and a desolation.

"Take care of my Roselyn," she begged, and her voice was a whimper.

"I have," I replied, "and shall continue to do so." But all implications of what I was saying were lost upon her.

I kissed Lucinda Jane with the feeling that I would never again see her in this life, but the thought was less a horror than a sweet, gentle grief. Farewells that speak of finality can be gruesome affairs. I left before the major arrived to drive her to the great docks where her luggage was already being loaded. I knew he would be sharing a fine, spacious bungalow with two of his fellow officers, an arrangement much preferable to single men's housing—or to living alone in a house that had once been a home. I wondered how soon he might take early retirement and join Constance, and how he would fare until then. I wondered. But I did not care as deeply as I would have cared a few months ago. There was no pain in my heart for his sufferings; he had killed that himself. Yet I wondered, as I walked back to my new home with Winston's hand tight in mine, if there was some lack in me, that I could cease my affections—roll them up and discard them like a soiled rug. Had I an unforgiving nature? A coldness I could not see? All I knew of a certain was the one truth: the major had broken my heart. Perhaps I had made too much of him, formed unrealistic expectations in view of Constance's lacks. I would never again hear those few kind words of praise that had woven the thin thread of sustenance through the years of my life: *We're proud of you, Lottie—we don't know what we'd do without you.*

I sighed, and Winston shaded the sun from his eyes to look up at me. *We are all learning to do without a number of things that are dear to us,* I thought, *even this quiet child here.*

"It is nearly teatime, Lottie," he said.

"Yes, and tea is always a comfort, Winston, isn't that true?"

I leaned over to kiss his cheek, and his hold on my hand relaxed a little as we walked into the house.

I decided to stay in Barrackpore rather than make the long journey to the mountains alone. I would have servants, it is true, but no husband to accompany me—and no Karan when I got there. The season was already late, and I felt sufficiently confident of my ability to manage the bad weather here. June would soon be upon us, and by midmonth, the monsoons. But I don't dislike rain half as much as some people seem to. Besides, Winston and I could keep ourselves busy within the confines of the house with no trouble at all. He was a great one for games and puzzles and make-believe. I was beginning to push back rusted, creaky doors in my mind which had been closed since my own childhood and cautiously explore the contents of those cherished storehouses. Winston came along for the journey—timid, unassuming, but his blue eyes like lights.

Then there was the library, a dim, silent treasure, whose splendors blinded me more surely than hoards of bright gold.

Here was my recompense, here my oasis, my soul's quiet delight.

As is the pattern of existence here, my hours with Geoffrey Hillard were few. I was forming a new life for myself, and he had a place in it, but he was not my life. I called him Geoffrey, but the name did not seem intimate. The intimate hours we shared were those dark bedtime hours. He had an appetite for such things that surprised me; he had seemed to harbor no passions behind his careful and proper facade.

We talked—more than most married couples, I'll warrant. He liked discussing with me topics that were usually reserved for gentlemen's conversations. I believe he took to bragging a bit, cocky in the fact that he had the usual pleasures of marriage, and much more besides. It *seemed* ideal, but something was lacking. There was no depth, no luster—perhaps a keen intellectual edge that could spark a sense of excitement, but beyond the expectation was nothing. All that I was, the real person inside, remained as lonely and solitary as I had been before.

The monsoons struck, churning earth and sky into one black cauldron. Rivers burst their boundaries, tearing chunks of earth with them. Streams of water wore channels through the parched desert; moisture seemed to seep up from the parched earth itself. The ladies cancelled most of their committee meetings; one could plan all one wanted to, but little could be executed during the rains. The majority of the women were safe in Simla, Darjeeling, or Mussoorie, anyway. The ones who remained were generally of the hardier sort, seasoned enough to guard themselves against the dread depression or lethargy which is a woman's most feared enemy in this place.

I was young and new yet, struggling to accustom myself to the servants' ways and accustom them to mine. Geoffrey had kept a larger household than I had expected. Each morning when I left my own rooms and walked out into the passage I would nearly trip over two *dirzees*, or tailors, who sat cross-legged, sewing on shirt fronts and gowns. The butler and *hamal* were not enough, he had a *mussaul* as well, whose job it was to polish lamps and silver and to wash not all of the dishes, but only the plates. In addition to Winston's ayah he had a *chupprassee,* or bodyguard, whose job it was to follow the child everywhere, though he had never come with Winston to my former house. I must admit, the man proved himself a good playmate, running after butterflies and climbing for birds' eggs and retrieving lost balls.

It was an elaborate system, this matter of servants in India which on the surface appeared well-structured, but was in reality a nightmare, a subtle maze. For instance, the *bheestee,* or water carrier, did only that: carry water from its source to the house. It was not his job to do more; indeed, it was unthinkable to expect him to fill a pot with that water or empty it into a plant. There was a *jemadar,* or chief servant, as well as a butler to oversee this intricate organization, but the memsahib must also understand what went on in her house. If the *wallahs* believed for a moment that they could get away with something, that the mistress did not have her finger firmly pinned on the pulse of things—well, then like willful children, they would attempt all manner of things.

So we struggled along through the sodden days, entertained by Mischief's antics, and doing our best to ignore the snakes coiled up in the bathroom sink; the muskrat curled up on the slippers at the foot of my bed, as timid as his more loathsome relative, the rat, is bold; and the mildew, more wretched than any creature, eating away at paper—the precious pages of books!—silk, linen, and cotton, the insides of boot leather, curtains and table coverings, and limp, slightly damp bedclothes. I loathed the creeping dampness more than any other feature of the season. But once one was outside, how green and transformed the world appeared!

"This is like England," I had heard many an officer's wife sigh, drawing the cool air and all of its fragrances into her lungs.

I liked it, too. Winston and I had our walks in all weathers, Vijaya, his ayah, and the tall chupprassee trailing behind. Some days we played games beneath the dripping trees until we were forced to scurry, soaked and shivering, back inside.

June passed in this manner, and most of July. Then one morning I awoke in the colorless predawn to a sound that sent chills crawling down my spine. At first I thought of hyenas and feeding tigers; then, as my senses cleared, I realized it was the high, keening sound of a woman's sobs.

I slipped silently out of the bed I shared with Geoffrey. He was a deep sleeper and did not even stir as the rope springs creaked and I moved about the room in the darkness, locating slippers and shawl and lighting a small oil lamp. I stumbled into the dim corridor, trying to locate the direction from which the sound came. In the back of the bungalow, stretched between the kitchen and the stables, was a row of small rooms where the servants slept. I never ventured there if I could avoid it. For, though nominally attached to the household, this was a world apart. Here the wallahs lived according to their station in the caste system, meticulously organized according to what was permissible and what was not: food, worship, dress, custom—all were prescribed according to ancient order, and into this world the white man did not intrude.

I slowed, hesitating, as my feet drew me closer to the unnerving sound. Then the door in front of me burst open and I drew back, startled. In the small, whitewashed room opened to my gaze, a woman, dressed in a white sari, the color of mourning, bent over the form of a man lying on a low cot. There was the grace of a swan in the curve of her body, and something about the line of her cheek under her shawl—

"Vijaya!" I cried. But the figure did not stir. I hazarded movement, closing the distance between us, and only then noticing the dim figures sunk into the shadowy corners of the room. One was chanting a prayer—to *Kali,* the chief Hindustani goddess. Or perhaps to *Shiva,* the god of birth and death. There are thirty-three million gods, goddesses, and demons whom the Hindus recognize and have to do with. I realized that I was as ignorant of them as most Britishers were.

On a small altar in one of the corners a woman was setting up offerings of fruit and rice and the fragrant jasmine, her low voice crooning in an almost inaudible singsong.

"Vijaya—" I reached out and touched her shoulder.

"My husband is dead," she answered in Hindi. But she did not look up as she spoke, nor move, nor even appear to breathe. "Leave me, memsah'jee, to grieve with my own kind."

She added the *jee* as a token of respect, but this was a definite dismissal. I backed away awkwardly, closing the low door behind me. The keening lament I had interrupted began to shiver into my ear drums. At this moment Vijaya was a stranger to me. I pulled my shawl up over my head and bent my back to the sound.

A death in the house. I shivered. I thought of Judith; I could not help it. That wraith of a woman who, even in life, made only a frail, slight impression before she sighed, and was gone. What had her short life been for? Of what use had it been to her—save for the small, confused child she had left behind her? Would she always—in some ineffable way—look out at the world through his wide, sea-blue eyes? And would she have considered that enough?

Chilled and shivering, I climbed back into bed. I was not yet accustomed to sleeping with a companion beside me. Even as girls, Roselyn and I had been given beds of our own. We shared a room, and the sweet solitude of girlish hopes and confidences, but we slept by ourselves. I pulled the covers up over me, but kept as close to the edge of my side as I could. There was something within me which I could not relinquish, though I did not quite know what it was. I refused to explore how much it might have to do with Karan. I hugged myself to myself, as the saying goes, thus increasing my loneliness and the distance that existed between myself and this man.

During the next few days I was largely excluded from Vijaya's life, and she was absent from mine. I mourned for her, but not in any way with her.

The third morning following her husband's death, Geoffrey stormed into the breakfast room dark with anger, so that the small scar between his eyebrows tightened into a fierce white line, like a scratch of lightning across his countenance.

"Do you know what that fool ayah of yours is intent on doing?" He spoke as though I myself had displeased or failed him.

"I have no idea what you are talking about," I replied.

"They're your servants, Lottie," he scowled, tearing a muffin open and spreading butter across the two halves. "Are you oblivious of what's going on right under your nose?"

I ignored the implications of his criticism.

"She's decided to throw herself on her husband's pyre—what do they call it, *suttee?*"

A cold fear crept through me. I sat down and gripped the edge of the table while Geoffrey poured out the tea.

"Don't look so stricken, for heaven's sake. We outlawed the atrocity several years ago."

"*We did?* The British?" I queried.

He glanced up at me sharply. "Listen, Lottie, the urge to be heathen runs deep in their veins. We do what we can for them." He lifted his thin shoulders in a dismissive gesture. "Surely you can stop her," he demanded. "Use your influence? Hasn't she been with you for years?"

I nodded slowly. My mind was moving painfully, beginning to churn out thoughts that were new to it. "I have no idea," I answered honestly. "I would never have dreamed—I thought I knew her . . ."

He snorted—a short, derisive sound that left no room for either defense or conjecture. "One can never know a native in the manner to which you are referring, my dear."

His tone was condescending, as though he were speaking to Winston. I thought of Karan, and shrank. I thought of my mother—of myself—and the coldness in my veins turned to fire. But he did not notice the lack of any response from me, nor even the expression that contorted my face.

"See what you can do, for reason's sake, Lottie. And remember—be firm. You are the one in authority." He kissed the top of my head. "I will check back before evening—this would bring a terrible disgrace on our house."

His words were a warning, though couched in friendly

terms. My first responsibility here was to protect his good name and reputation; my second, to establish my own. Vijaya did not come under consideration.

I continued my round of morning instructions to the servants, then sent Winston off to the park in company with his ayah and bodyguard. And as the moments brought me closer to a confrontation with my old friend and servant, my dread of the moment increased. With a clarity that overwhelmed me I realized how little I knew her, and how little I had wished to know. She had been placed there *for me,* and all that had ever seemed necessary to observe or understand fell within the compass of that one dimension of her being. There must be so much more! As I pondered, our experience on the boat came back to me, and I cringed inwardly; that was the first time I had ever wondered about her as a person. Yet how many times had I turned to her for love and reassurance, for wisdom and strength? Always asking, assuming, commanding. *That is the way of it,* Constance would say. *She is your servant; she expects nothing more.*

"But she is also a woman," I whispered out loud, to the dripping garden. "And she loves a man enough to sacrifice her own life. . . ." The stark words refused to be said. They played out in my mind, a horror I could not imagine—an injustice my shocked senses refused to take in.

Perhaps it *was* only household rumor, with no substance at all. Perhaps Vijaya, when I approached her, would wave me away with a light laugh, and that would be the end of it. With these vague hopes to bolster me, I at last sought her out.

She knew at once, before I had spoken a word; and in that instant when our eyes met, the truth was revealed. The naked horror of it made me gasp and put my hand to my throat.

"It is true, then?" I asked. "What they have told me?"

She only nodded, and though she did not drop her eyes, a tenderness crept into her gaze.

"You wish to do this, to sacrifice your life . . ." *To be burned alive!* The words screamed in my head, and I knew she could read them behind my eyes.

"*Sati*, we call it," she said. "It means 'virtuous one.' Such is the wife who chooses to join her husband—you must see it that way." Her voice was low and persuasive; her eyes still held mine. Had her senses already been drugged by some opiate to deaden awareness? "I will join my beloved and pass from this life, and all will be well with us." The golden lights in her brown eyes glowed.

How do you know this, and how do you know what comes after? I wanted to scream. Instead I said, to my utter amazement, "You cannot die. I need you, I really need you, Vijaya." Just like a child, falling back into the pattern learned in my cradle, before walking and speech.

She shook her head. "You are stronger than you know, missysahib. You can stand without me."

She had called me the old term; it was not lost on me. "The Christian religion teaches that life is sacred and that no man has the right to end it before *God chooses!* He alone knows when the end has been reached, when the whole length of the road has been trod."

Her calm eyes, watching me, said, *Why do you tell me such meaningless things?*

"Vijaya, think! Will you pray to the gods and consider again?"

"To what purpose?"

My mind was frantic. What could I say to her? My thoughts were not hers. We had lived for many years in a close and affectionate harmony, yet in some ways we stood worlds apart.

"There are realities you must consider, and honor of a different sort."

The wariness in her eyes told me she understood my meaning.

"The British authorities will not allow you," I said, knowing as I spoke the words how true they were. "The ruling is a new one, and they will not be thwarted. They will make an example of you."

Her eyes darkened; all the gold lights went out of them.

"You know I speak truth. Rather than the fulfillment you seek, you will find only humiliation in your world and dishonor in ours."

I knew my words were blunt, but I have never known how to be subtle. The muscles of her face shifted; I watched them rearrange themselves into a mask behind which all her anguished emotions were safe.

"Please, Vijaya." I placed my hand on her arm. "Give it up now, of your own accord, while that choice yet remains."

She said nothing; she looked out from the mask and said nothing at all. After a few moments I turned and left her. Throughout that long day no further communication passed between us, there was no sign from her, no clue offered concerning her intentions. When at length I dismissed her from her remaining duties she slipped off like one of the shiny lizards that has slithered in from the rain.

In the late afternoon a small squadron of uniformed officers rode up to the bungalow and dismounted. I stared out through the curtain of mist to watch their noisy approach. I knew what they wanted.

"Did my husband send you?" I asked.

"We are here on his authority," the captain replied. "Sorry about this whole business, missus."

How thoroughly he misread the distress in my eyes! I let them search the house and the servants' quarters, but I was not surprised when they returned with no sign of their victim. Now they squirmed with discomfort, reluctant to return and report to Major Hillard; I did not blame them at all.

I sat alone, picking over my light meal, and waiting. I had tucked Winston into bed, with the usual songs and stories. I had written a letter to Constance, and then torn it to bits. Why did the major not return? He had never been this late before. At length I shoved the food away and went in search of my sketch pad and some sticks of fine charcoal. I must draw Vijaya's features before they dimmed in my mind! With a sense of urgency that made my hands unsteady I scratched the first marks. I must limn well those strongly moulded cheekbones; the mouth, large and full lipped; the soft, curved chin line that gave a feminine feel to her face. I tore up half a dozen sheets of paper and let them fall to the floor—extravagant waste here in the heart of India! The servants had disappeared, perhaps sleeping; but I doubted it. I must get this right! Her face was as clear, as crisp in detail as if she stood at my side. But my skill was so clumsy, so lacking!

At last, trembling with disappointment, I stretched my arms out and hid my face against them. Where was Vijaya? What was Geoffrey doing? The questions went round in my head, until their torment at length exhausted me and all my senses went numb. I did not hear the sounds—the footsteps and the voices—until they were nearly upon me. I jerked my head up with a start, my eyes darting about the room, but unfocused yet. The first thing I distinguished was Geoffrey's voice. The tone was high and excited; there was an exultant laughter laced through it.

I ran my fingers through my hair, then remembered the papers and quickly scooped them into a pile and shoved it under the desk. I could hear the scraping of many boots in the entry and the low tone of men's voices. I braced myself, my hand on the tall chair which partly concealed me. I thought of it as a comforting barrier—against something; I was not sure what.

Geoffrey strode into the room, like the master he was. For the first few heartbeats I did not recognize the filthy, crouched creature that he pushed before him.

"It took us nearly all night to find her." Geoffrey's voice was slurred with pleasure and, I suspect, with strong drink. "A right nice little caravan, with priests and oxcarts and burning incense, heading straight for the Ganges—weren't you?" He clapped his hand upon the woman's shoulder and shook her so roughly that she fell to her knees.

I bit my lip so hard that the salty taste of blood filled my mouth.

"Get to your feet!" Geoffrey growled.

He half raised his prisoner by a jerk on the strap that

secured her hands behind her. Her feet also were bound. I could see blood on her wrists and a long purple bruise along one of her arms.

She swayed, but she somehow remained standing, with her eyes on the ground. I stared at a point somewhere above her head and below Geoffrey's chin.

"The general consensus, my dear, is to throw her into jail and let the authorities deal with her in their own good time." He drew himself up with an assumed dignity that nauseated me. "It is my opinion, however, that she should be turned into the streets to beg for her keep—as an example! Surely no one will ever hire her after this."

He was so smug. The men that clustered in a knot around him partook of his arrogant mood. I put my hand to my stomach, afraid I might be sick right there.

"My opinion is that the lot of you ought to be clapped in irons and shipped back where you came from! What crime has this woman committed?" Eight pair of eyes stared at me, blank and somewhat stupified. "What crime?" I persisted. "Save that of following a time-honored religious conviction. She is worth all of you brutes put together!"

I could hear my own voice, almost as something apart from me, and was surprised at the resonance and power that vibrated through it. "Release her at once! This night's work is a disgrace on all your heads!"

With indignation running like a fire through my veins I lifted my eyes to meet Geoffrey's. "Vijaya is *my servant,*" I said. "Brought from Major Reid's household, paid through his dowry allowance; she is no burden to you." I drew a deep breath and stood as straight as I could, though every muscle in my body was aching. "She will, therefore, stay here and maintain the honored place she has held—and deserved—in Major Reid's household since the time I was born."

The whole room seemed to hold its breath when I ceased speaking. My own breath caught in my throat, and I knew my gaze must not falter, not by the most imperceptible movement, if I was to carry this off.

Seconds passed, but they crawled over my skin like an agony. Then I heard a low, soft whistle and a shuffling of feet, and Geoffrey was cursing me roundly, but with a grin on his face.

"She is quite the little vixen, is she not?" he pronounced proudly, slapping his nearest comrade resoundingly across the shoulders.

"She is a fine, spirited woman, she is," the man agreed, raising shy eyes in my direction.

"Out of my house—at once!" I commanded, trying to bark like the major did. They turned like so many docile school boys and filed through the door one by one.

I turned without looking to see what Geoffrey was doing. With my arms around her I half-supported Vijaya's weight as we walked from the room, through the long, chilly hall, until we came to the servants' quarters. This time, dazed and weakened by the ordeal I had been through, I *was* surprised.

A low lamp burned and a table beside it sat ready with cloths and ointments and a basin of sweet-smelling water. Soft brown arms gently removed my burden. Vijaya was laid on a bed of soft rushes, and half a dozen bodies bent over her and hid her from view.

I stood alone—stranded, staring awkwardly, but unable to do anything else.

"Come, missysahib. Kind hands will take care of Vijaya. I will help you back to your room."

It was Radha. She, too, had used the old term, made me feel like a girl—tender and so terribly vulnerable. I felt tears burn in my throat. I swallowed against them and leaned on her arm.

"I can manage now," I said, as we reached the door of the bedroom that I shared with Geoffrey. My voice was no longer strong. It sounded like an old voice, and very tired. "Will you kiss her for me? Will you tell her how much I love her?"

"Oh, missie!" I felt Radha's warm lips brush my cheeks, then she scurried down the passage and there was nothing left but the shadows.

"Charlotte—dear—is that you?"

Geoffrey's voice crawled along my skin. I was too worn out, too hurt to reason the matter. Something in me knew that there were masters who were strict, even cruel with their servants. And who could fault them, when they might easily use as examples the native peoples themselves? Cruelty, to the Indian, was an art. They flayed men alive—put their eyes out—cut their hands off for some minor offense. The Englishman was *civilized;* that was a recognizable and indisputable fact.

I pushed the door and walked across the threshold. "Come to bed, Charlotte. We can sort all this out in the morning."

My mind cast about wildly. "I—well, you see, Winston was frightened earlier in the night. . . ." I swallowed; even such small lies sticking like glue in my mouth. "He begged me to sleep with him, and—and I think we've disturbed him again—"

"The boy will be fine."

"No. I believe I'll just crawl in with him. I don't want him fussing later and waking us. Heavens, what time is it now?"

"Off with you then." He yawned. "We'll sort it out in the morning."

I closed the door on his last words and slipped gratefully into Winston's small room. The child slept soundly, his little fist curled like a flower against his white cheek. I drew back the covers and lowered my body beside his, grateful for his warmth and his softness. I was crying now, weak, ineffectual tears. I closed my eyes against the tears, against the horrors my mind still held, cupped like some bitter poison, ready to spill over again.

Chapter Fourteen

THE FOLLOWING MORNING GEOFFREY slept late, but I arose early, having not really slept at all. In the light of day, last night's scene seemed preposterous, and all that was left of the little girl in me longed to imagine it away; or worse, minimize its realities to a point where they were acceptable and the edge of horror frayed and beyond recognition. I dreaded the prospect of a confrontation; dreaded, too, my first meeting with Vijaya, dreaded to look into her eyes.

I went about the usual tasks of the morning. The sky was an iron-gray expanse, stretched taut and impenetrable, like my mood. Winston could sense that something was wrong, especially when I bundled him off for the second time with his two guardians. His wide eyes questioned me, but he would not go beyond that. I kissed his cheek.

"Will the sky ever again be as blue as your eyes are?" I teased, and had him smiling before I banished him to the nursery. Then I waited, uneasiness gnawing at me. The servants went about their tasks with an unaccustomed silence. Even the empty rooms of the house seemed expectant. I sat in the front parlor with my embroidery on my lap, my head as dull as cotton wool, and my eyes burning from lack of sleep.

When Geoffrey entered I felt every muscle in my body tighten and a sick sensation rise up in my throat. *This is ridiculous,* I chided myself. *You are not a child about to be scolded.* And yet, the first words he spoke seemed to belie me.

"Have you anything to say concerning your behavior last night, Charlotte?"

I swallowed my shock and indignation enough to reply to him in an even tone, which was necessary if I were to hope for his attention at all.

"Yes, I am amazed at the equanimity and presence of mind I displayed."

In some perverse way my answer delighted him. "You are certainly a woman of parts, Lottie," he replied, and pride was evident in his voice.

"We must strive to communicate," I said, thinking it best to ignore the direction he was taking and the condescension it may lead to. "Your behavior has disturbed me deeply."

He took a seat, crossing his long legs in front of him. "In what way, my dear?"

"Do not insult us both by resorting to word games, Geoffrey. Some men are capable of cruelty, and some are not. I saw last night that my husband is one of the former." I waved his protest away before he had begun to speak it. "Rights, justification, necessity—I am interested in none of that."

"Now you're talking like a woman, Lottie," he countered, and the words were an accusation.

"Not as bad a thing as you claim," I responded, attempting a smile.

"Do me the courtesy then of telling me what it is you want of me."

"I want to be able to trust you again."

He dismissed the complaint of my heart with a gesture. "There are certain things you simply do not understand—"

"I understand this well enough, and you know it." I set down my sewing and rose to stand before him. "I will leave you," I said, "if such scenes as last night are ever again enacted. If I find repeated reason to mistrust you . . ." I wanted to add "fear you," but I dared not speak those words out loud.

He did not laugh or dismiss my statement this time, though most men would have. "You are serious, Charlotte?"

"Yes, I am."

"Then I shall have to tread a little more carefully." He

spoke the words under his breath. His eyes examined the length and breadth of me, as though taking my measure. "I am willing to readjust perimeters and understandings between us," he conceded. His eyes, moving over me, were keen with appraisal, neither cold nor warm. For the first time since I had married him he *seemed* older. It could be Major Reid standing before me, or one of the senior officers who had forgotten what youth was before I was born. "All right, Lottie. We'll speak more of this later. I am already hours behind."

He turned and left me. *What am I doing here?* something within me cried out. I returned to my chair and sat, limp and unseeing, with no incentive to move, no idea of what to do next.

The encounter had gone better than I had dared to hope; indeed, it had been a success. He had not shouted and attempted to bully me, he had instead made concessions that might prove vital. But in the end, what did that matter? He had not said: "I am sorry to have hurt you, Lottie. Forgive me." It had not been in his eyes. Nor had he spoken the words "I love you." Did none of that sentiment exist in his heart? Was I incapable of sparking that vital emotion in him?

There must be some love, my mind reasoned with a sudden, cruel clarity. *If he does not love me, and I do not love him, how can we hope to survive? Love builds and succors and sustains. What does lack of love do?*

I had no answers for my own questions. I felt not only drained, but depleted. Aware of a rustling at the entry, I lifted my eyes. Vijaya stood before me, composed, dressed in her workday sari, with not a line or fold out of place. But I knew in an instant that the strange instinct which had driven me the evening before had been for a purpose. What my clumsy strokes had captured on paper of the old Vijaya was all that remained. This ageless woman who stood so calmly waiting had been inexorably altered, as I had been myself. My face burning with shame, I shifted my eyes to meet hers. Nothing could have been more startling than the acceptance and peace I found there. Words were not necessary; words certainly would not serve well, but I had to try.

"I cannot excuse—I cannot even explain men like Geoffrey Hillard," I said, and the sorrow in my voice was as liquid as tears. "Life has added weight to us this day, but perhaps together we can carry the burden, and remain—apart."

She nodded. The tenderness in her gaze reached out to me.

"Ah," I sighed, "who am I to speak to you of such things? You have lived that way for years." I paused. "You will stay?" I needed to ask the question.

"I will stay here to help you." She glided across the room and came to stand close beside me, placing her hand on my head. "Together, as it has always been." Her eyes spoke what mine were afraid to: *We stay because, what choice have we? Where else have we to go?*

The winds that churned the dust and the rains finally dropped, and the flaccid air rested. The leaves that remained on tree and vine hung sodden and limp. There would still be squalls, but the monsoon season was ending with the promise of cool, quiet days ahead. It had been three weeks since Vijaya's return to us, and a harmony, at least on the surface, had been restored. It was midday when the butler interrupted my reading to announce that I had a visitor.

"Sahib Reid," he said in response to my raised eyebrows.

"See him into the front parlor, Ali," I directed, struggling to control the sudden racing of blood to my heart. *Something must be wrong, terribly wrong, for the major to come here,* I thought as I followed the servant. But I knew I must show no hint of distress until he enlightened me.

I entered the room. The man who had been father to me stood in obvious discomfort, his legs far apart, his hands folded in front of him.

"What is it?" I asked.

"You look lovely, Lottie," he said, attempting to smile at me. "I hope you fare well."

"I fare tolerably, thank you," I answered.

"Good," he replied, ignoring both the obvious and the implied. "I had a packet of letters last week from Constance."

I could not help it; his words could still strike pain in my heart. She had not written to me once since her departure for England, though I had already sent off several letters to her and the boys. Why had she severed me so completely from her consciousness? Did she realize her power to hurt me, or was she somehow beyond that?

"Does Lucy still thrive?"

"I believe so," he replied, reservation in his voice. "She had trouble adjusting to the English climate—at first, that is. I believe she is all right."

I wanted to ask about the boys, but I feared that my voice would tremble, and since he offered no comment, I simply asked, "And what brings you here?"

"I've come to say good-bye, my dear. They're sending my men off on a march, and I may be gone for some months."

Such marches were common procedure; indeed, when convenient insurrections were lacking, these proved the only means of keeping the soldiers in shape. But why this formal departure? Did he fear for his health? I felt that he hid something from me.

"Well, sir, I shall miss you," I said frankly, "and wish you well as you sally forth to challenge India." I knew I must keep it light, light and friendly between us.

He laughed politely. "You take care, Lottie," he said, and moving quite suddenly for such a large man, he leaned over and planted a kiss on my cheek. With a bluster and a cough into his sleeve to cover the moment, he began to make his escape.

I watched after him, curiosity vying with apprehension. The nearness of him, the scent of the lime cologne he splashed over his cheeks each morning, brought a sudden rush of childhood memories that were more sweet than bitter, and something in me longed to rush after him and throw myself into his arms, the way Roselyn and I used to when the wrath of Constance threatened us. But all that was past. The kindness in his nature was no longer turned toward me. He no longer had the power to comfort, to protect. He had forfeited that for things he deemed of greater import.

"God go with you," I said, wishing he was close enough to hear me, not realizing how soon I would question why he had not spoken that blessing on me.

"Transfer?" I repeated the word woodenly, because as yet it had no meaning for me.

"My division has orders to report to Baraset, about the same distance north of Calcutta as we are west."

"Must you go?"

Geoffrey stared back at me. "Of course I must go. What's come over you, Lottie?"

I was not sure. Men could be transferred from station to station on little more than a whim. I myself remembered several in detail: Lucknow and Agra and Delhi before Barrackpore. Why was this feeling of loss and frustration assailing me?

"How soon do we leave?"

"Within the week."

"Then you must have known of it and not spoken to me."

"Nothing was confirmed till this moment."

"Why have you not spoken to me?"

"Lottie, for heaven's sake! This has been your home for so long; I was not sure how you would take it."

Of course, he was right. And that was the basis of the misery I was feeling. In leaving Barrackpore I would be leaving all of childhood behind—leaving that family and home which would never again be restored to me—leaving the last of Karan. Here he had breathed and spoken, here he had walked; I could point to the trees he had leaned against, whose shading branches had sheltered him. And, touching them now, I could feel the sense of him vibrating through me. When I turned my back and walked away from here, all that would be gone. Even the major—Major Reid! Awareness surged through me. Of course! He had known! Geoffrey had confided his plans to his old friend, but not to me. And the major had not possessed the courage he needed, commanded the kindness necessary to bid me a proper farewell.

When Geoffrey arrived home that evening, I tested my theory. "Does Major Reid approve of your regiment's new appointment?" I asked.

"He thought it splendid. This is a choice location, these small posts around Calcutta."

I dropped the subject, and he did not pursue it, nor think to apologize for not including me in knowledge of his plans sooner, as he had the major.

The following day, however, he appeared at the door sometime midmorning and announced bluntly that our plans had been changed.

"We're being posted to Dacca. It will be only temporary. We are to relieve the Twenty-sixth, a crack regiment who had been sent there for disciplinary reasons."

I had heard of Dacca, up in the Bengal wilderness. "It would be madness to go."

"No more than a year, Lottie. I have the governor-general's word on it."

"And what is in it for you?" I was beginning to know how my husband's mind worked.

"A possible promotion in rank, without having to purchase it; such has been hinted at broadly. And *batta*. The batta is higher nowhere, save in Sind and other of the more far-flung regions."

This batta, or allowance paid for hard lying or discomfort, could as much as double an officer's regular pay. I could see the calculations going on behind Geoffrey's eyes.

"I do not believe it is worth the risk," I said. "You must know the frightful percentage of men who die there." To add "women and children" would have no power to sway him.

"It is a calculated risk I am willing to take."

You are willing! I bit the words back. A woman's place beside a man to whom she was committed, because of the love she bore him, would be trying enough. But under these conditions, it was nearly insufferable.

So be it, I said to myself. He will not get the better of me, nor have the satisfaction of seeing me come crawling or whining.

Pride should sustain me, if nothing else would. I set about getting things in readiness, but beyond the organizing of servants and their tasks, there was little to do. And, secretly, I was glad of it. I felt weak and lethargic, and put it down to my depression of spirits brought on by the move itself and the state of my personal life.

The day of our departure, a servant I recognized from Major Reid's household appeared at my door. I watched his approach from my vantage point in the garden, and wondered vaguely what errand could bring him here. Not bad news, I hoped sincerely. Early in the morning there had been an hour of rain. The air was sweetened by it; the dull coating of dust washed from trees and grass and from the pale, anxious lizards that slithered among the slick stems.

Vijaya did not bring the servant back to where I was, but dismissed him and came with his message herself. She carried a packet bound up with cloth and string; it looked like a book of some kind. She held it close for a moment, then extended it to me with a very solemn expression.

"This comes from the major," she explained. "He left it in the hands of his butler with instructions that it be given into your keeping if you were to leave Barrackpore before his return."

I ran my fingers over the faded material, which was hardened with age and worn to threads in pieces.

"Did he say what the package contains?"

Vijaya's eyes studied my face for a moment. "It is your father's journal," she said.

I heard a ringing in my ears, and the scenery before me shifted and blurred. The last thing I remember distinctly was the sight of a large, wet crow, swooping off his perch on one of the limbs of the banyan, his immense wings, glinting green and purple, shaking a spray of water over everything as he stretched them out wide.

Chapter Fifteen

I OPENED MY EYES TO SEE Dr. Fielding's profile outlined against a yellow shade. I lay in a darkened room—my own room. But the bed that held me was makeshift, and the room was empty save for us two.

He turned, sensing my wakefulness. "Are you feeling any better, Lottie?"

"I believe that I am." With one elbow I raised myself up, and he built a support of firm pillows behind me. "What happened?" I asked.

"You fainted—which is not like you," he added. The gentle, crinkled smile lines about his eyes lifted, and one corner of his mouth twitched. "Yet it is altogether natural for a woman in your condition."

I did not know what he was telling me.

"You are with child, my dear."

My hand flew to my mouth, and he chuckled softly. "Now, Lottie, do not appear so surprised. You must have guessed—"

But I hadn't, not really. "Has something gone wrong?"

"No. I suspect you have overworked yourself. That, along with the strain of leaving here and . . ." He paused. "That alone could have done it. But I understand there was more." He rubbed a long finger against the stubble on his chin. "I understand you received quite a shock out in the garden."

I nodded, not realizing that my eyes filled with tears. "My

father's journal, kept all these years by the major, and intended for me. Yet he never told me a word about it."

"The man may have had his own reasons."

"I am sure that he did. But whatever they were, he meant for me to have it before leaving this place. Yet he could not bring himself to give it to me in person. I cannot understand why."

I could not yet separate my shocked astonishment at holding my father's book in my hands from the heartbreaking awareness that the major had left under false colors, as they say, and was willing to delegate such a precious task to a servant.

"Forgive him, if you can," Dr. Fielding said, placing his hand over mine.

"Do you know where we are going?" I asked.

"Yes," he replied, and I could guess from his voice his thoughts on the subject.

"Is Geoffrey terribly angry at this delay?"

"He had better not be. I have advised him to wait a few days before thinking of submitting you to travel, but he will not hear of it." His face twisted into a lopsided expression that was only part smile. "He has conceded you one day, at least. You are to leave in the morning."

"Resting in a palanquin and taking the journey in slow stages," I added. "Do not worry, Dr. Fielding. I would rather have it this way. I am keyed up for leaving, you see." To stay here on pinpoint . . . I thought of the farewells I had taken, of Roselyn's sweet, quiet grave, and all that lay dead there beside her.

He nodded his head. "Of course. Vijaya will take good care of you; we both know that."

"I shall miss you more than I can say," I told him. "I wish you could deliver this child."

"The gods are never so kind to us," he replied, not pretending that his feelings were any different than mine.

"Have you heard anything further of Karan?" I asked, feeling a trembling go through me at the spoken sound of his name.

"Nothing, I fear—not even sure confirmation of what I told you earlier. But I shall keep my ears open—no, I shall make definite inquiries, and then let you know."

Someone cares for me, I thought. *This thin, tired man with the eyes of a savior, who knows more than one manner of healing.*

"You must not do that."

"Nonsense. I will if I've a mind to. *He* cannot stand in my way." *Nor yours,* his eyes added.

I smiled up at him. "God bless you, dear friend. You will perhaps write then? You will not forget me?"

"Lottie!" His hand still rested on mine, and now he twined our fingers together. "We are kindred spirits," he said. "It is not a matter of forgetting. You see, I believe that such souls, though parted, are never truly separated."

I leaned my head against the incredible strength of his seemingly frail body. *It could have been you,* I thought guiltily. *You are unmarried, you are of an age with my father. It could have been you—except that no one marries their daughters to poor, worn-out doctors. Heaven forbid! Instead, instead . . .*

I fell back against the pillows and closed my eyes and managed to keep from crying until I heard the doctor's footsteps go down the front walk.

As it was, Geoffrey provided not a palanquin borne on men's shoulders, but a gharry, pulled by Cinnamon and one of his horses. Two passengers could fit in a gharry, stretched out on a mattress, struggling to ignore the constant jostling over uneven roads. Usually my companion passenger would be Vijaya, plying me with yogurt and raspberry tea and strange-smelling herb concoctions that were meant to be good for me. At times Winston was allowed to ride with Mother; Winston of the sea-blue and troubled eyes.

"You are ill," he said the first day, snuggling close to me.

"Yes, but I am not going to die."

I could feel his disbelief, like a coldness between us. I reached my arm out and drew him close. "This is not a dying kind of sickness, my dear one. Can you keep a secret?"

He nodded warily. I whispered into his ear, wondering what he would really think of the tidings.

"Is it true?" he asked solemnly. "There will be a brother for me?"

"Yes, a brother or a sister for your very own—and I shall be happy if this baby is half as nice a child as you are."

He knew I meant it. Children can seldom be deluded by adult protestations, especially where love is concerned. He relaxed. I could feel the poison of fear leave his body. *I have made one human being happy,* I thought. *One little boy knows what it means to be happy, and to hope. And this is because of me.*

It was the one comfort I had. The trip that would normally seem only tedious was grueling for me. I could not keep food down, and yet if my stomach was empty I became ten times as sick. My head throbbed with the dust and the dizzying motion. Because of me we traveled slowly, with many annoying delays, taking nearly six weeks to go a distance usually covered in three. At designated points all along the route there were relays of fresh men for the palanquins in our company, and horses for us. At length Cinnamon was relieved of active duty and tied behind one of the oxcarts. Geoffrey and most of the men traveling in our company rode elephants, and though we were a small caravan, we stretched into dozens of animals and hundreds of men and servants. My memories of the journey are dim: bones that ached nearly as much as my back did; the taste of bile in my throat; grimy, cheerless *dak* bungalows where I laid my dizzy head down to rest; and Vijaya's hands, always Vijaya's cool hands administering quiet relief. I remember one time passing close to a native village whose people had never set eyes on white men before. They all ran away, melting into the wild country around them, and the air of instant desertion was absolute and eerie. I *felt* like an intruder, sensing nothing in common with these villagers who looked upon change with horror, who had been living the same ancient pattern through generations of time. No matter that I carried traces of their blood; their ways were not inbred in me. The conquering race that was destined to alter their existence held sway in my life, and it seemed to me I had no say in the matter at all.

Near the end we took some stretches of river travel—wide rivers, deep and swollen, that seemed like seas. We all arrived in a state bordering exhaustion, at an outpost so desolated that any spark of possible enthusiasm died in our breasts. There were several empty, unoccupied houses, so the foremost concern of locating adequate living quarters could be easily satisfied.

We were given temporary rooms in the cantonment until the house we selected could be put in order. And that very first night the outgoing regiment gave us a ball; less to welcome us, I suspect, than to celebrate their own release from this shadowy region of suffering and death.

I am not much for society, and I was yet weak from the journey, so I tried to beg off. But Geoffrey insisted I attend—"even for a few moments," he said. "It is crucial you do."

I dislike strangers and dislike crowds, and I had barely the strength to hold my head up, but I was determined to do him proud. My own pride drove me to it. Our clothes were all terribly wrinkled and smelled of mildew, but I had Vijaya air my watered blue silk gown, which sat well against the honeyed shades of my skin. I washed my hair and let her and Radha arrange it in piled curls on my head, where the rich shades of chestnut and red would be highlighted. I had grown a bit thinner these past weeks, and the loss of weight gave me a pale, almost diaphanous appearance that fit in well with the place. I noticed heads turn when I walked in on Geoffrey's arm, and I noted how much more pleasure this impersonal admiration brought him than it did me. We danced once, then he took me to a chair and ordered a punch for me. My head was spinning, yet I remember thinking that the lights were not bright enough nor the music gay enough to drive away the murky darkness and the clinging shadows.

Nevertheless I smiled at the young men who gave their hands to me, and even danced with a few. And I flirted, because that was what Geoffrey was doing with a choice selection of the officers' wives, those of the outgoing company, who were strangers to him. He could strike a fine figure if he wanted to, and tonight he wanted to. Perhaps he was bored. I watched him, deep in conversation with a woman ten years my senior who was leaning so close to him that her blonde curls brushed his face. She was very pretty, with porcelain, doll-like features. I watched as he placed his hand on the small of her back and led her onto the dance floor. It was easy to see that they were enjoying themselves. The faint buzzing in my head began to grow louder. I smiled up at the young lieutenant who was watching me.

"If you will take it slowly, Mr. Sheldon, then I would be happy to dance with you."

He led me out, skillfully clearing a place for us among the other couples, holding me in a tender, tentative embrace, as if he feared I might break. He was a nice-looking boy, with a fine forehead and a strong, sensitive mouth. I surmised that Geoffrey's mouth was weak from what I had seen of it, concealed as it was by his full, long mustache. I had never liked the mustache; yet, thinking about it, I shrank from how his face might appear without it.

I liked this boy. I liked the subtle rum scent of his cologne, I liked the warm touch of his hands. I felt a childlike sense of regret when we parted. I forced myself to dance three more times. Then, nearly reeling with weakness, I walked out into the night air and found Geoffrey's man and ordered him to bring the carriage round and take me back home.

Atop a small rise that appeared to brood over the huddle of barracks and bungalows that comprised the station stood two large, roomy houses, set in beautiful gardens. Geoffrey took one of these. Some of the sepoys came to him with rumors that both houses were haunted and it would bring the sahib and his family bad luck to dwell there, but he paid them no mind. Two weeks after our arrival it was finally ready for me to move into. Because it was large and had more rooms than we needed, I had ordered separate bedrooms made up for myself and the sahib. When Geoffrey questioned me, scowling so that his white scar showed livid, I managed to answer him with a natural, almost nonchalant air.

"I am ill yet, as you know, and suffer nausea, and toss and turn much during the night. It is thoughtless and senseless for me to disturb your rest. I can keep Vijaya with me, to be of assistance until this child presents itself."

What could he say? I had reasoned on his behalf, not my own. I was learning, but I regretted acquiring those skills which would only increase the terrible loneliness of my life.

We moved into the house on December 8, a Thursday. The following day was my father's birthday. I was now nineteen, having passed that milestone on an October day in the gharry. I was now five months with child, aware of the growing life within me and feeling an age away from the girl of a year ago. I felt at my neck for the familiar chain and the shape of the ring. I had already determined that on this day, symbolic as it was, I would open the packet my father had left for me. The apprehension I felt was nearly as strong as my eagerness. What if I did not like what I found? What if it did more harm than good? I had organized the household to run smoothly without me, and sent even Vijaya away. In the square, sunless room I sat in the rose-flowered easy chair I had brought with me from my former house. It had been the major's chair, but he had often told me that I had sat many times in this chair with my father when he was alive. With my fingers I untied the loose knots and pulled away the wrappings to reveal a thin leather journal with my father's name engraved on the front: "Frances Simmons." I traced the letters slowly, reciting under my breath what little I knew of him. Sun-gold hair and a laughing mouth, and green cat's eyes. I remembered his eyes. I could feel the tenderness of them, a memory I had folded a long time ago with great care and put very gently away.

I turned back the cover. This *was* a journal of sorts, though the entries were quite irregular, the dates on the first two pages ranging from August of 1816 to December, 1818. Places leapt out at me: Agra and Delhi; one entry from Simla:

The fishing fleet have arrived en masse, hovering about like so many brightly-clad butterflies, so pretty and eager to please. Each man among us could have his pick. There are two, in fact, who have caught my fancy—but neither draws my interest. *I know I am not easy to please.*

I scanned the pages, searching for one particular date. It jumped out at me, because he had penned it in large, bold letters, and underlined it as well.

6 January 1817: Today I had a strange, very intriguing encounter: I fell in with a young gypsy girl. I had been out exercising my horse and stopped along the roadside to remove a stone from his hoof. She came from the direction of the small village which stands hard by, where she had, I assumed, been selling her wares, the assortment of baskets and bangles she carried with her . . .

I closed my eyes. I must be able to draw this for myself—I wanted to see it, as if it were happening to me.

She began to flirt with me. Because of her beauty and the mood I was in, I found myself flirting back. "Shameless thing," I told myself. "She is more child than woman, and probably knows no better." I turned to go, but in doing so noticed that the colored scarf she wore wrapped around her arms and shoulders was stained with blood.

"You are hurt," I said, and she froze, her frightened eyes appraising me.

"If you would help me, sir," she said, "I will take no advantage."

Her voice was like liquid music. I helped her up onto my horse, supporting her frail weight with my body. Alan Fielding is with her now. He is to be trusted; though heaven knows what I shall do with her!

Dr. Fielding! He had never spoken of my mother to me. Yet he had been part of their lives from the very beginning!

The next entry was much later—17 March 1817:

The hot season advances upon us, and most of the women in the station are making plans to escape. Sita Beg is still with me. Her gypsy friends have long since departed—Crim agents, I now feel sure. In fact, I believe she was spying out a house and was caught in the act, and in this way received her frightful injury. How could this gentle spirit be part of such things? Ah, but she does possess the sharp, clever mind which the Crim caste so admire in women. She will not yet speak much concerning herself, but my curiosity grows. Under guise of a servant, I keep her close to me. She invades my library with regularity and can speak the Queen's English if she's a mind to. There is something strange and powerful which draws me to her!

"Draws me to her," he said. The next entry came nearly two months later:

11 May 1817: I am at this moment a most happy, well-contented man. Sita has told me the incredible facts of her life—at least what she knows of them. They place her at good advantage. To think of the life she has lived! And what if I had not been here to provide her a means of escape? But, best of all—after much persuasion—she has agreed to become my wife! Believe me, I have never fancied myself with a bubu, *a native wife. But she has done what none of the fishing fleet could manage: she has fascinated both my intellect and my heart. She is the perfect companion—the harmony between us is something one would read of in books. I love her with the kind of emotion I never imagined existed.*

I put the volume from me, face down. So, it had been true. This mystical union I had fancied between them had been quite real, after all. Both had ignored opinion and custom and listened to their inner voices instead. If my father had been living when Karan came into my life . . . I picked up the slender volume and began reading again. He missed few of the highlights. He told of their marriage and the support he received from most of his friends. He told of going to some of the wives when he found out that his Sita was going to bear him a child, and appealing to them to take her into their circle and accept her. What a difference the appeal of the sincere, charming young man must have made! On that cool October morning when I came into the world it was Dr. Fielding's hands which guided me. He had been part of the brief, sacred circle of our lives. He would remember. He would describe my mother for me. But he was no longer here. I might never see him again to ask the questions that burned in my heart.

I read hastily. My birth took place in the last part of 1818. My father was thirty-one when I was born, but how old was the girl who slipped in and then out of his life so quietly? For two fleeting years they lived the life of the blessed. How quickly that time must have flown! I flipped through the dates. I knew nothing of the end of my mother's life, or how she had died.

"29 January 1821," the date read. I noticed that the writing in this entry was small and crimped, as though the forming of each individual word had been painful.

> *I write what I must. We have suffered a small epidemic of cholera in the camp. Four nights ago I was away from home, in company with several other officers assisting Dr. Fielding in his gruesome tasks. It was past three in the morning when I arrived home, dog tired, to throw myself into bed. Sita was gone. There were signs of a terrible struggle which had left the room in a shambles. I roused the servants at once. To a man they claimed ignorance of the matter—no one admitted to hearing a disturbance at all. We began an immediate search in all directions. It has now been three days. There is no trace of them—even in the beginning they had left scarcely a sign. It is as she had feared, poor child! Yet I thought after the passage of three years we could consider her safe! The Crims had need of her services and hotly resented my interference—especially one man who had for a long time been attempting to persuade her to become his wife. Is she with him now? The thought drives me to madness! I know they*

will not be unkind to her; they hold her in such high esteem. But this cruel blow—this living death—is more than either of us has power to bear. I do not sleep, I do not eat—despite Alan's urgings. My mind feels unhinged, my body hot and fevered—but the torture in my heart! My helplessness to restore my dear one to safety!!

With a broad slash of the pen his entry ended. The journal slid from my lap. This was too cruel! I had believed her safe and buried! Instead this nightmare unfolded before my horrified gaze. I sat with my hands clenched in my lap, my eyes dry, but burning like hot coals in my head. No wonder my father had become nearly insane with the agony of it! No wonder that the pain had tortured him into a shadow, robbed of substance and purpose, desolate of life!

I felt the touch of hot liquid against my lips before I realized that Vijaya stood at my side. I let her force a few mouthfuls of tea down my throat before I pushed her away.

"You knew!" I accused. My voice was no more than a croak. "Yet you remained silent, like all the others."

"It was not mine to speak."

"Get me the book," I ordered.

She bent over and picked it up from the ground. "Rest for a while before—"

I shook my head at her. She lowered herself to the floor and sat, cross-legged, gazing at me.

"Leave me. At once!" I commanded. But she paid me no mind.

I turned the pages. I forced my eyes to focus. There were no more entries for a long time. The next was dated nearly a whole year later.

3 January 1822: I have set rewards for the return of my Sita and sent out relays of men—soldiers lent to me by the commanding officer, and native sepoys well trained as local scouts. I continue the search from month to month, but no hope is ever offered in the empty cup of my days. I have depleted my means, I have alienated myself from the ordinary people around me whose lives have continued forward while mine has been caught in this stagnant pool of despair. Lottie is three years old now. I believe she still misses her mother as she did the first months when she cried continually, "Mata! Mata!" *and held her little arms out. But the few memories she has will fade, and in time die altogether, and she herself will be all that is left. But in this child the mother's eyes will shine forever, and the fine, gentle mind will be guided by virtuous thoughts.*

His tribute to both of us. If only I could remember! If only he could be with me again!

"22 March 1824." My father's last entry.

I leave for Rangoon with Sir Archibald Cameron next week. I have volunteered for his Burmese campaign, one of great import to the British, and of no little danger, as it has been explained to me. If there be a god in heaven I pray he will lead me to the honor of a soldier's grave and the peace I seek—which only Death can now grant.

The Burmese War. It had now become a bright star in Britain's history, because it ended in victory, despite the immense loss of life. My father had been there when Campbell took Rangoon in May, only to find that he must push far inland to penetrate the center of power, while the Burmese soldiers, expert in the use of "digging in," disappeared by the thousands into their hidden stockades. By a stroke of luck, their ferocious leader, Bundoola, was killed by a shell, and never replaced with a man who could match him. So, despite raging cholera and high losses, the British pushed on. Eventually the enemy capitulated, but the cost was six out of every seven English soldiers, and as my father had wished, he was one of those casualties. His struggle had ended. But what of the gentle woman whose nightmare had only begun?

There were a few remaining lines on the last page—an afterward, scrawled perhaps before his leaving on this final journey:

I have placed Lottie in Ralph's keeping. He is to be trusted. He has a daughter, Roselyn, near her own age. Perhaps they can grow up as sisters, and my child will know something of love. She is an Indian—but what does it mean to be an Indian? There are so many shadings of caste and race in this land. And though some claim otherwise, a woman fares ill here. I hope fervently that she will escape and live an English life—and every lovely petal of her mind and spirit will be opened—as I would have seen done for my Sita if—

His words broke off there. But it seemed I could feel his tormented thoughts churning round the room, echoing and re-echoing in tones of sorrow. I could not catch my breath. I tried to call out, but only silence answered the frantic pleas of my heart.

The last thing I remembered was Vijaya's pale face above me and the feel of her hands on my arms—small, strong hands lifting me, lifting me—before I slid into oblivion and darkness, and peace.

Chapter Sixteen

THE SMALL BLACK FACE belonged to a wizened old man, I was certain. For was not his beard long and white, with tufts of cotton fluff stuck to his chin and trailing in wisps round his face?

I blinked my eyes and rubbed them with my fists, like a child. The round face with the pointed chin focused into Mischief's familiar features. He sat atop the bedclothes, staring up and blinking back at me. Winston sat cross-legged beside him. I tried to smile, but the muscles of my face did not seem willing to move.

"Have I been in bed long?" I asked the quiet-eyed child.

"Oh yes, for these many long days." His cheeks were as white as the sands that the blue sea stains. "You nearly slept straight through Christmas. Vijaya said that you might."

"That was most unthoughtful of me. But here I am, you see. And I shall be fine."

I attempted to lift my head from the pillow, but the effort sent sharp pains piercing through my forehead. "Where is Vijaya?"

"I am here, missysahib." She materialized from one of the shadowy corners, and at a nod from her, Winston slid off my bed, pulling the unwilling monkey with him.

"Have I been ill?" I demanded. "What is it, Vijaya?"

"A touch of brain fever, they say. Rest and liquids, and no excitement if you are to keep the baby."

"Bring me pen and paper," I said. She did not move. "Bring it!" I demanded.

"Not yet, memsahib." She had called me "missysahib" only a moment before, reverting, as I also was wont, to that happier time.

"It is important. This letter should have been written days ago. Make haste, Vijaya."

With a sigh she did my bidding. But by the time I was propped up in bed, my muscles felt as weak as a kitten's and I could not guide the pen. I dropped it petulantly, the ink staining the coverlet. Clucking disapprovingly under her tongue, Vijaya swept it all up and away from me. "Perhaps later," she said, and the tenderness in her voice frightened me more than anger would have.

I did not get out of bed for Christmas day, nor for the loud celebration of the New Year. The fever and weakness would not leave me, nor the terrible headaches. If I pushed too hard my throat would constrict and I would find I could not speak or call out, but must lie gasping for air, frightened and unattended.

Nights were by far the worst. I slept alone; the pallet that served as Vijaya's bed lay in a small extended alcove of the room, several feet from my bed. In the darkness I would fancy I heard footsteps, and even the sound of voices conversing in low tones together—flat, tired voices that sounded incredibly sad. Once I heard crying, followed by a hideous laughter that set my whole body on edge. I would lie trembling, soaked with sweat, afraid to cry out, too weak to move. In the morning I would put it all down to the wild imaginings of my vivid mind and my fevered brain.

Bit by bit I mended, and the doctor began to have hope for me, until one night when I fancied I heard my mother's voice calling out to me. I remember that I stumbled from bed, supporting my weight by leaning heavily on the pieces of furniture, and in this manner, moving from place to place. The voice continued. It seemed to come from somewhere in front of me, drawing me on. I must find my paper and write to Dr. Fielding; he would know what to do. I was certain that if I asked him, he would come and deliver my baby. And more important, he would tell me about my mother! I was sure that he knew—knew the story of her origins that my father had alluded to. I must get him here!

I floundered in the darkness, cracking my knee against a sharp edge of some sort. With a cry I went down. Vijaya was there, almost before I hit the hard floor. And so was the voice. Now it seemed to come from a vague, insubstantial figure that hovered just below the ceiling near the foot of my bed. I struggled to move. Vijaya's arms were hampering me. I struck out like a child.

I do not remember what happened next, save for the pain and the light. I was struggling for breath—struggling for sight—struggling against the great weakness that was holding me down. I remember the voice floating in and out of my consciousness, but I could not tell what it said. I remember fear like a gray blanket laid over me, fear as intense as the pain. Somewhere Vijaya was whispering to me gently, but the voice had more strength. And the voice was winning—and the voice was part of what frightened me.

Everywhere was the gray smothering blanket—then a thin crying sound, helpless and hideous. Then blackness again.

The next time I awoke, it was all over. I knew it, without anyone saying a word. I lay very still, so as not to attract Vijaya's attention. I felt lighter in my body, and strangely light in my head. And I knew everything was over, and they had taken my child from me.

"What did they do with my baby?" I asked Vijaya, still not moving.

"It has been days. The major would have disposed of his body. But at last he allowed me to take the child and bury him according to our custom."

She, too, sat still where she was, watchful, holding her breath lest she distress me.

Geoffrey walked into the room. If only he had not walked in at that moment, might the future have been different?

"You are awake," he said, trying to make his voice sound pleasant. But though his quick glance traveled down me, he would not meet my eyes.

"I am sorry," I said. "We had a son—I am so sorry I lost him."

He looked at me then, unable to disguise his own feelings. And his gaze spoke so clearly that I sucked in my breath at the blow. *I expected more of you. This madness—where does it come from? You were so composed and clever, so much my equal.* He was looking at me differently, as though there was something in me which he abhorred. *This native blood!* I could almost hear him say the words. *It has rendered you unfit . . .*

He stopped, aware of how deeply I comprehended what was passing between us. "You will heal," he said, "and there can be others."

I said nothing, but I would not lower my eyes.

"At least I still have one son," he said, turning from me.

"*We* have one son," I corrected him. But he did not turn back. I was to remain without comfort, without succor, without a friend.

I could not rally. I would try to gather my strength, my inner resources, but they would fall apart in my hands. This helplessness, this lethargy frightened me. I had never been patient with such weakness in other women; how was I to abide it in myself? I lay abed for hours, only rising for brief periods every day. The inactivity itself seemed to create a cycle of weakness. My head felt always light and a little dizzy, which put my whole world out of kilter. Vijaya ran the household, together with Geoffrey's steward and the butler, whose special job it was to oversee the other servants. And all went well. Things went on smoothly without me. Even poor Winston adjusted to being with Mama only a few moments each day. *I was not needed.* The realization was awful. I sunk into the aura of gray that seemed to surround me, with no will to struggle against my fate.

"It is this house!" I heard the servants whisper—at odd

times when they were performing some task in my presence and did not seem to realize that I had the power to hear. "Black magic has bewitched the mistress—the bad spirits who hide here . . ."

Their covert words made my skin crawl. Could their superstitions be true? I knew how deeply the Indian believed in the evil places where bad souls roamed and were not at rest. Dacca was such a place. And this house—was it haunted? Had something terrible happened here to draw the spirits of unrest to inhabit it?

At night, when darkness seemed to claim all existence, I could feel the restlessness about me. And at times the sound of voices, toneless and hollow, seemed to rise from the ground and swirl, like a heavy mist, threatening to suffocate me. The voice I had thought was my mother's—had it been a trick, a hallucination contrived by these tortured spirits whose only delight was to visit their own misery upon others? I did not know. Alone in the darkness, while Vijaya slept, I tried to imagine the child, torn early from the womb that should have nurtured him—thin, wrinkled limbs and a sunken chest, and small, sightless eyes that would never gaze upon the face of his mother. I could not push the vision aside. It was part of the darkness, silent and secret, that possessed these hours and left me exhausted and shaken when the pale morning came.

So went my days, that somehow became weeks. And then the heat came, marching in from the plains. And the heat brought its own kind of madness, which was not restricted to me. The men languished; many of them sickened with fevers. The insects were thick: beetles with shiny, hard backs that made a slight metallic sound when one struck them; the lines of ants; the slithering centipedes; the hoards of mosquitoes, buzzing, always buzzing. The punkahs creaked day and night. The thick air, wrung of the slightest tinge of moisture, trembled like gauze in the sun's rays, shimmering down from a white, cloudless sky.

One day in late March, Lieutenant Sheldon appeared in the doorway of my drawing room, standing nervously awaiting admittance, shifting from foot to foot and twirling his hat in his hands. Winston peeked out from behind him, and that is when I suspected that something was afoot.

"The young sahib begs only a few moments," Vijaya murmured at my elbow, "for something very special."

I frowned at her; she had been instructed to screen all of my calls.

"Please, Mama!" Winston bounced.

I demurred slightly, with a cautious nod of my head. My visitor came forward, and as Winston followed him, I could see that he carried some small creature partially wrapped in a cloth, and cradled in his small arms.

"For you," Winston said, holding it forward.

"He is only days old," Hugh Sheldon added, "and needs a kind home."

The flying squirrel stuck his tiny, pointed muzzle against my fingers. It felt warm and moist; his eyes were moist and golden, and flecked with wonder. I held out my hand.

"The lads up yonder don't know how to care for him," the lieutenant added gratefully, as though the matter had been settled. "And I hate to abandon the little fellow. His mother and several others were—"

"Shot for sport!" Winston blurted when the young officer hesitated.

I shuddered. I knew that winged bats are often found in modest flocks; I had noticed hundreds about this house, hanging from the old trees like shreds and tatters of dirty old rags. I had seen the wide-spanned flutter of their featherless wings shadow my path. But the flying squirrels were a different and happier breed.

"This one's young enough to train to go free, without a cage. They're not hard to manage. He'll eat any little tidbit you can save for him, especially fruit."

"*Cha?*" Vijaya asked, bringing the tea tray in unbidden. I scowled again and sent Winston off with the creature to discover a suitable bed for him.

"Did you know I live right up the hill from you?" my visitor asked, balancing the delicate teacup Vijaya handed him on his knee.

"The other large house just past here? Not alone, surely?"

"No, indeed. There are six of us who share it."

"And is it haunted, too?"

My guest stared for a moment, uncertain just how much to tell me. Then, attempting a cavalier laugh, replied, "I cannot vouch for it myself. But some of the others have heard and seen some quite remarkable things."

Was I only imagining that he watched me too closely? Did I only misgive the look of caution in his light hazel eyes?

"Do you believe them? Do you believe in the—supernatural—the reality of spirits?"

"Do you?" He bent close. He was not baiting me; his question was a sincere one. I caught a tinge of the rum scent I remembered from the night of the dance.

"I do. One cannot believe in good without believing in evil."

He *was* watching me now, but for a different purpose.

"Something happens to the soul of us when we die. There must be more to *Life*—than this clumsy and narrow existence."

I tried to smile, without succeeding. I took a sip of my tea. He was not moving.

"Your words make sense," he replied. "But is the realm of the spirits so near to us?"

"I believe it could be. I believe men do not change when they die, not really. What was good remains good. What was evil . . ." I shrugged. A stuffy closeness seemed to be building around us, hemming us in.

"Can a spirit cause harm to a mortal?"

"I am not sure. Perhaps *directly* he cannot, because he is no longer corporeal. But there are other ways . . ." I paused again. I was growing uncomfortable and unbelievably weary. Vijaya appeared at my side and took my half-empty cup from my hands.

"You have been ill," the lieutenant said, "and distressed. I have been most sorry to hear it." Before I could stop him, he reached for my hands, holding them lightly in both of his, chafing them gently for comfort, as he might do with a child.

"This is no place for a woman like you." He spoke the words under his breath so that I guessed at them, rather than heard them. But his eyes made no apology.

"I am stronger than I appear," I answered him.

"Then I am glad of it," he said, and let my hands drop, and replaced his empty teacup on the tray. "I must be going now." He glanced in Vijaya's direction, aware of her dark eyes watching him. "I hope the flying squirrel will prove helpful, occupy your attentions—"

"It was very thoughtful of you." I spoke with what feeling I could muster. I wanted him to know of my gratitude. "Winston and I will try to take good care of him."

He nodded. "I have no doubt of it. For now, then, Mrs. Hillard. Perhaps I might call again?"

"By all means. Vijaya, show the sahib to the door, please."

She followed after him with her usual quiet shuffle, which is really more of a gliding movement that pleases the eye. I watched both of them until they disappeared through the doorway. Then I rang for a servant and sent him in search of Winston and our new toy.

The squirrel slept in my room, in a nest with an excess of pillows, thanks to Winston's zeal. I called him Shadow because, like a bright nymph, he shadowed my every move, the most coaxing little creature I've ever seen. Winston delighted him; they drew delight from each other. But Shadow seemed to both adore and need me, creating sensations in my breast that had lain dormant for months. Many nights I would awake to find him perched on my pillow, softly licking my face. It was a foolish notion, I admit, but I looked upon him as a guardian spirit of sorts, a good omen which stirred something long still within me.

The heat built, like the gradual increase of temperature in an oven, scathing and scorching, until we felt our very brains would shrivel up in our heads. The fruits of India grew ripe and luscious, and the flying squirrel thrived. But the men in Geoffrey's company began dying like flies.

One night he came home late, his hair wild, his face despairing, and despite all, my sympathies were drawn to him. "Over half our men are in hospital," he said. "Would to heaven Dr. Fielding were here!"

"What can be done for them?"

"Precious little. The fever must in most cases run its course. That and cholera, with more holes when we stand at muster each day!"

I wanted to say: *Take care for your own safety,* but I could not get the words out. Just what did I feel for him, standing tired and distraught before me, his mottled hair clinging like wet moss to his face? What did he feel for me? We seldom spoke to each other, save for the polite amenities which were expected, which kept the smooth routine of the days moving on. He seldom asked after my health or my activities; perhaps my madness had truly frightened him. He spent long hours away, gaming with his friends, sometimes drinking heavily. Perhaps it was, after all, better that we asked no questions of one another.

The next morning I sat down to my desk and wrote my long-delayed letter to Dr. Fielding. As I wrote I heard the raucous cries of a blackbird, repeated in throaty demand, just outside my window.

Grim crow, I said to myself, *I shall answer your demand and not quell, whatever the response might me.*

I felt better. I had never felt stronger since my arrival in Dacca. I began taking Cinnamon out very early in the mornings. Even at half past four it was oftentimes difficult to catch a breath of fresh air. But the rides did me good. I went earlier than any of the other women, scant in number as they were, who inhabited this inferno with me. Some of them I was acquainted with from Barrackpore days, but due to the various conditions I had suffered since my arrival, we had done no social visiting back and forth. My sole acquaintance and companion, as it were, remained Lieutenant Hugh Sheldon, the quiet young man with the hazel eyes. He was circumspect, entirely proper, but I knew that his feelings ran to greater depths than he showed. And for this reason—remembering—I felt compassion for him, and allowed myself to enjoy his company and the modest attentions he showed me.

So we made it through April into May, taking it almost one breath at a time.

One May evening, after a day of unusual oppression, when the white sun boiled in the heavens like the very furnace of judgment, I heard my husband enter the house, and something about his footsteps—the quick, light pattern of them—alerted my senses. Though the hour was earlier than usual, most of the servants had retired, and the great empty rooms hung with that silence which was peculiar to them. Shadow had been curled up on my shoulder; I remember that I put him aside. Vijaya sat on a rug near my feet; with a few curt words Geoffrey sent her away. Then he turned to me, the tendrils of his wheaten hair curled on his forehead, the set of his mouth grim beneath the drooping mustache.

"It has been too long since we have been alone together in one another's company," he began, trying to coax a warmth into the words. I took his meaning at once, but said nothing. "You are looking much better, Charlotte. Your cheeks have color again."

"I am glad you notice," I replied, forming my own trap.

"Oh, yes, I notice. And so do others, I hear."

The words were spoken lightly, as a jest. But scarcely concealed beneath them was a deeper meaning, and an implied threat which made my blood boil with its audacity. Still I said nothing at all. This maddened him, but he must struggle for control yet a while longer.

"Here, my darling. I have a present for you."

He brought out a large box which he had set just inside the entrance. "Open it," he urged, with some impatience. "I believe you will like what you find."

I complied, with a stir of curiosity despite myself. Dacca is a place known for its gauzelike muslins and silks delicately embroidered in silver and gold. Odd that such beauty should thrive in such desolation. My husband had gone to some lengths to obtain the fine cloths I now ran through my fingers—exquisite!—making my skin ache at the feel of them. And the colors were as delicate in shade as the fabrics themselves.

"Thank you," I said. "They are lovely—too lovely." I swallowed pride and fear, like gall in my throat. "It is a most generous gift, Geoffrey."

He waved my weak thanks aside. But he did not say: "You are deserving of such gifts." He did not say: "For you, anything, Charlotte." And there had been a time—a time before the loss and the madness—when such words would have come to his lips.

"The seamstress shall make them into lovely gowns for you. They will be light and cool."

There was a satisfaction in his voice which made me feel lonely, somehow alienated from him. "Why don't you take them into your room, dear? I will be along directly."

He turned from me, stroking Shadow's thick fur, assuring that no argument, not even a reply would be offered him.

I rose from my chair. I had no choice; I knew that. I walked slowly through the long hall, past the cavernous rooms where only shadows stirred. I felt the fine fabrics rustle and shift in their box. My own spirit, like a captive bird, fluttered, pale and futile, against its invisible cage.

Chapter Seventeen

LIFE ALTERS. IT IS NEVER STILL and stagnant, as we think it. Much like the air of the desert which appears suspended and lifeless, it yet breathes with a life of its own and moves through us when scarce we know it, and alters our course.

Shadow thrived, Lieutenant Sheldon continued his visits, and Geoffrey demanded his rights as a husband. Then in May, Winston was struck with the fever. I had his bodyguard move all his things into the small room adjoining mine. I stayed with him day and night, taking my meals there, reading, pacing, praying. There were no more morning rides. When Hugh Sheldon could cajole the servants into admitting him, I made a minor concession and sat with him on the chintz-covered chairs in my room, with the door ajar, and Winston's ayah beside him. I realized how much I loved the child. He seemed a part of myself, and at the same time, something more. The young woman who had given him life looked out sometimes from the blue, childish eyes. I felt beholden to her. So much would be lost if he were to die.

Vijaya worried about me. But I felt no return of the weakness, only this awful constriction around my chest, a white-hot panic that would at times rush through me demanding action, resolution—demanding release for us both. Geoffrey said little, but the lines about his eyes deepened, and the scar below his forehead seemed more jagged and defined.

The days passed. There was no measure of time in this vacuum. I watched, interrupted by brief intervals of sleeping or eating. Sometimes I read. Sometimes I sang soft songs to the child who tossed and turned on the bed, his struggle for life consuming him so that he scarcely recognized I was there. But one morning I awoke to find myself on my own bed. Who had moved me from the narrow cot that sat beside Winston? I raised my head, confused, and beginning to be angry. My stomach turned over and I knew I was going to be sick. And despite not wanting to, I knew the reason why. To be with child—now! here! I lay back, trembling, feeling a fine mist of perspiration break out on my face. I wanted to cry. I wanted to bury my head in the pillow and never look up. But the days of madness were too soon behind me, and they frightened me more than any of the surprises life held closed in her hands. I struggled up. I would not succumb! Not now. Not ever again.

Winston clung on tenaciously, and the days grew imperceptively cooler. Shadow sat on the dressing table glass each morning watching me dress and do up my hair, with his unfathomable black eyes fixed on my face, his little paw held out for my hand, that he might draw it up and bite at it playfully. And Geoffrey asked each morning concerning the state of his son, but stayed later each night over his billiards and drinks. I did not tell him of the knowledge I carried within me.

One day Lieutenant Sheldon presented himself quite early in the morning, and I was surprised to see that Vijaya had let him in, until I glanced up and saw his face, gray and unshaven, reminding me at once of my brothers when they were still young, frightened boys. I bid him enter and take his customary seat beside me, but he could not hold still, and rose and began pacing the length of the carpet.

"What has happened?" I asked. "What is it that distresses you?"

"I have no right to say! To burden *you*." There was such genuine affection in his tone that I felt my heart go out to him. "Only let me stay here beside you, for just a little while."

I placed my hand on his arm, and the touch seemed to

instantly calm him. "Please tell me," I urged. "I am up to it. And anything that diverts me!" I glanced toward the open door into Winston's sickroom.

"You mean it?"

"You know that I do." He had the finest eyes I have ever seen on a man, delicately shaped, almost like a woman's; they mirrored a soul that was guileless and devoted to that honor which he believed to exist in the affairs of men.

"Two of the lads up at the house above—you know, there are only four of us left."

"I did not know."

"Two have gone to hospital. And last night Andrews died. I was with him. It was horrible, Charlotte!" He had taken to calling me that. Though I knew Vijaya disapproved, I permitted it. "He screamed and raved at the end, not wanting to let go, fighting against it!"

"I am sorry. I am sorry for your sake."

My expression of sympathy again soothed him. "After he died, I went home. I walked through the darkness, recoiling from entering that house with the smell of death upon me!" He shuddered. "I cursed myself for a fool, and in that way gathered my courage. I nodded to the sepoy on duty and vaulted up to the porch. When I pushed the door open the first thing I saw was Alan Taylor sitting at a desk with his back to me. He seemed to be scribbling something, but when I called out to him he did not answer. Then, for the first time, I noticed that he wasn't alone. Another man stood on the stairs above him, an officer of rank. And the two seemed to be conversing together, but I could not hear what they said." I saw a wild light leap into his eyes at the remembering.

"As I hesitated, not knowing what to do," he continued, "the stranger descended the remaining stairs and walked past me. He was a tall man, Charlotte, and well proportioned, and he moved with the slow confidence of authority. As he approached the front door, I turned from him and rushed to where my friend sat motionless. A horror was building inside me, a feeling of dread. I grasped his shoulders with the intent to shake him, but he slumped forward in his chair, his head falling onto the desktop, his eyes wide and unseeing."

I felt Hugh Sheldon's horror thrill through me. "Your friend was dead?"

His eyes gave his answer. I reached for his hands. They were ice-cold in mine.

"Then there is no course but one. You must quit that house—and at once!" I told him, not attempting to hide my concern.

"But that is not all," he said. "I ran out the door to call back the man, to enlist the aid of the sepoy who guarded the door. The stranger was nowhere in sight. And when I questioned the soldier concerning him, he claimed that no man had passed him—no man had come out of the house. I questioned him gruelingly, but I do believe he saw nothing—nothing at all!"

"Well." I chafed the cold hands automatically. "You and I know that such things can be. It is of no good to question them—and certainly less to attempt to explain them. But, Lieutenant Sheldon, you must get away!"

"Yes, I must." The excitement seemed to drain from him with that concession. "For there is yet one thing more. When I walked back to Tom Fenton's room I found him burning with fever, in a state of near delirium. I had him moved to hospital, and then I came here."

"Poor boy," I muttered, trying to think, trying to get my mind round the facts. "You and one other remain untouched entirely?"

He nodded.

"Then take steps at once. Arrange for quarters elsewhere. Turn your back on the tragedies that have been enacted, and try to forget."

"I shall," he agreed. His voice had dropped low, become gentle. "And you?"

"Me? I shall be fine where I am; you may rest certain of that."

"I do not."

"You are distraught, shaken by what you have been through."

He closed his now-warming hands over mine. "If there is the slightest chance that any harm might befall you . . ."

With a gentle firmness I removed my hands from his clasp. "There is no evil in this house, only memories and shadows."

He was not convinced. He sat beside me at last, gazing woefully upon me.

"Then pray for me," I said, wondering where the words had come from. "Pray for all of us here—in the tenderness of that kind, trusting heart of yours."

My words moved him to pain. "Is there nothing more I can do?"

"No, my dear young friend. Life has not granted you any greater power than that."

I met his eyes and realized, with a shock, that he was, though young, definitely older than myself, who was offering him the wisdom of the ages. But, oh, at that moment I felt age-old and well used by life.

After he had left I went back into my son's room and sat by his bed. I had tried everything, save what I had told the lieutenant. I was not a stranger to prayer, but I felt a stranger to that Being toward whom prayers are directed. And yet, what harm could it do? Might not the Christian god take pity on these least of his children, stranded on the sands of India, alone and in need of succor?

I closed my eyes. I sensed the hollowness in the rooms around me; I felt hollow inside. Of their own accord my fingers felt for the token that hung at my neck. *Love was the power.* How could I have forgotten? Was Karan's love with me still? My father's? The woman's whom I had once called Mother? I had to believe it was so.

I began to pray haltingly, inside my head, then whispering the frail words out loud. I took Winston's hand up and held it against my breast, willing my love and strength to flow into him. I sat thus a long time, every energy of my soul concentrated upon the desire that had induced me to importune heaven's deaf ear.

I must have dozed off. When I opened my eyes, Winston's blue eyes were watching me, unclouded and clear.

"Mother?"

I leaned over and kissed his warm cheek. "I am here. I will stay by you." I thought of that first time I had come into him and watched by his bed, and tears came into my eyes.

"Do not cry, Mother. I am feeling much better."

I could see that he was. I would not let myself believe that my prayers had made a great difference—surely such things could not be. But I tucked the memory of this pure moment away, deep inside my sore heart. *I will remember,* I vowed. *I will not fail to remember this day.*

The dust, perhaps more than the heat, had made it impossible for me to spend much time in the gardens. Now, with the first of the rains, I sought to pass every cool, undisturbed moment I could there. Soon enough the monsoons would blow, and render the whole world too wild for habitation.

Lieutenant Sheldon was true to his word. He and his one remaining comrade moved into the barracks with the other men of his own rank, and his spirits seemed to settle a bit. Winston gained strength daily; children have such resilience. I continued to hedge with Geoffrey, reluctant as I was to bluntly tell him that I was expecting another child. I knew part of my reluctance was tied to my vulnerability in my relationship with him; I fancied that my delicate state would place me more in his power, and less in my own. For that reason, too, I refused to think of this new life growing within me as anything real at all. So many things could happen that had power to rob me of hope and promise, and I did not wish to go through that again.

I procrastinated and demurred for so long that I forfeited the moment, and it became Geoffrey's, not mine.

One morning early, while we sat at breakfast, he said bluntly, "You pick at your food, Lottie. You have done so for weeks."

I looked up at him. "How long have you been with child, then?" I swallowed the bite I was chewing and tried to form my words carefully.

"Are you not happy?" I said.

"You might have told me." The words were a growl.

"I did not wish to worry you. Winston was still so ill when I discovered it—"

"But you have been quite well yourself."

"Better than last time, thanks to Vijaya's administrations."

I did not say it to goad him, but he scowled. He still accepted her presence in his house only grudgingly, representing, as it did, his humiliation and a rare moment of power for me.

"Perhaps this is a good omen, then."

Did he mean the words kindly? Were his intentions toward me better than he was able to show?

"Are you pleased at all—does the idea of . . ." I could hear myself stammering.

"Babies are for a woman's pleasure, Lottie. Men take pride in their children, but babies . . ." He, too, was searching for words.

We both wear veils, I thought, *but for different reasons. What is he hiding from me? For a time he revealed part of the inner man to me, but now even that window is closed.*

"Tell Cook his *badan pasindah* was terrible. The lamb was tough, and he seasoned it so lavishly with paprika that I nearly choked."

He had turned the subject; that was the end of the matter. So inconsequential a thing, so little its impact upon the world he inhabited.

"Will you be home for dinner tonight?"

"Major Hawley and his wife have been pressing us to accept their latest invitation. May I tell them Thursday?"

I nodded. "Yes, I believe that will be fine."

He had not answered me. That meant he would probably drink his dinner over cards, rather than eating it with us. I did not feel like pressing him. His absence in my household was of small moment to me. But eating alone, with an army of servants waiting upon me, was such a lonely affair.

Later in the morning I sent Yusaf with a message for

Lieutenant Sheldon, asking him to dine with me that evening. I knew it was a rash thing to do. But it turned out a blessing. When I arose from my long nap in my screen-darkened room, there was a letter waiting for me; Vijaya brought it in on a tray. It bore a Barrakpore postmark and a hand I recognized. Alan Fielding had received my letter, and I held in my hands his reply.

It required long moments before I could work up the courage to slit the envelope open and draw the weighty sheets out. I unfolded them carefully, smoothing the creases. "Will you leave me, Vijaya?" I asked.

She did not reply, but sat down a few feet away from me and drew her folded embroidery work out from a drawer by her side.

I read the greeting, which would be safe enough: "My dearest Lottie, how can I convey my joy at seeing a letter from you—and then my anguish to read the words it contained? How am I to answer without causing you further sorrow?"

I had not told him of my illness, of the breaking apart of my inner resources; the gentle humanity in him would have unconsciously altered his responses, and I did not wish that.

"Are you well? I pray that your child was born safely and that both of you thrive—"

Were he to know! Were he to know! How I ached for his sympathy! I tightened my shaking hands into fists at my sides.

"Yes, I was there at your birth. I assisted your gentle mother; I watched you draw your first breaths of life. But I thought you *knew.* Surely Ralph must have told you all that he could."

A coldness swept through me as the memory of my parting with Major Reid swelled up in me. I put one fist to my mouth.

"I was transferred shortly after your mother's disappearance and did not cross paths with you again, as you know, until Barrakpore. You were then a young woman, with the shadows of the past well buried, or so I supposed."

I sighed, and Vijaya's eyes flew to me. "I am all right," I assured her. "Attend to your work."

"If Vijaya has told you that she does not know the history of your mother, then she has told you the truth. I suspect there were fewer than a handful of us with whom your father shared it, possibly only Ralph and myself. It is a story worth telling, despite its own tragic sadness. I only wish I were there at your side to hold your small, soft hands in mine for the telling. Try to imagine me there. You are good at such things, and you trust my affection enough to do as I ask."

I closed my eyes and let my head sink back upon the soft cushion; he had set me a pleasant task. I would not find it difficult to call up his lean, sensitive features, nor to fancy his voice speaking aloud the words he had written.

"What do you know of the Sikhs?" he asked on paper. An innocent enough question. I could recite my mind's store of facts concerning them: the sect began in the early sixteenth century under the leadership of a brilliant mystic, Guru Nanak. He cunningly drew upon the best of Islam, he enticed the Hindus of the *bhakti* movement, and with their strength, formed a religion of great spiritual intensity. As Karan explained to me, the Sikhs believe in only one god—a revolutionary concept in India. Their way promises serenity, repose and purification, or at least it did until the Englishman came. They were already turning from peace lovers into a warlike people who held as an ideal the warrior-saint. This I knew, but little more of the religion. Of the people themselves, I knew how tall and well formed, how skilled as fighters the men were. I knew of the incredible power and wealth of the ruling Singh family; I had seen them, bedecked in fine pearls and emeralds, ride past upon hundreds of elephants, each more splendidly adorned than the last. I knew of the barbaric uses they made of their power, that the number of persons in their territory without noses or ears was legion, and that it had been rumored that one of the chieftains had actually flayed alive three hundred men who had offended him. This I knew. But I did not know what Dr. Fielding was about to tell me.

"The Jumnoo family to which the Singh rulers belong," he continued, "hold their women in great respect—did you know there are female Sikh warriors as well as male? Ironically, however . . ." He seemed to draw his breath and hold it, and I found myself doing likewise. ". . . it is the practice of that family never to allow a female infant to live. They marry wives from other high Rajpoot families, but refuse to give their own daughters to what they consider inferior princes. And, of course, to live unmarried would be unheard of. Hence this heinous practice of putting away these precious innocents as soon as they come into this life."

I covered my face with my hand. I was aware that Vijaya was watching me, though I had not made a sound. I could not imagine—I did not want to try to imagine! "Have you guessed?" he went on. "Your mother is one of these infants who was spirited away, perhaps sold to the Crims or some other, by a young royal wife who could not bear to snuff out the life of her infant. I know, dear, that the picture is grim—past imagining—I fear, perhaps past bearing for you! One wonders how many such infants there are. If the mother suffered wrath at the hands of her husband for her deed, we do not know. Chances are, she was able to cover her deception and go on as before, except for the terrible secret she carried in her own heart."

Oh, yes, the heart, which is capable of breaking over and over again, yet still going on!

"You can imagine better now your father's tender protection of her, the state approaching awe which he held her in—" I smiled to myself. "And Sita. You can imagine the heaven that his love was—the amazing freedom of her life with him, laced through with a kind of respect she had never imagined, much less experienced—"

I threw the sheets from my lap, as though suddenly the touch of them burned me. *To have it all snatched away! But then I, too, know something of having one's life stolen by the hands of another, do I not?*

There was a commotion outside the door, and a servant entered. "Sahib Sheldon is here ahead of himself," he reported, "and begs admittance."

"Yes, the memsahib will see him at once."

The servant had bowed himself out before I could turn on Vijaya, venting all my pain and frustration. "How dare you!" I shouted. "Your insolence grows insufferable!"

"Does mine as well?"

I glared at the young man who stood, hat in hand, regarding me.

"I felt an urgency I cannot explain," he apologized. "As though somehow you needed me." He was embarrassed to speak the words. "But I see I have intruded," he added, and began to back from the door.

"Not at all, sahib." Vijaya was on her feet now, the serene mistress again. "The memsahib has great need of you. She has just received the most distressing of news."

I dropped my eyes. I could not hold onto my anger. Hugh Sheldon took a few steps toward me.

"Is it true?" he demanded, while his soft hazel eyes searched my face.

"It is true. But it is none of your affair." My voice sounded harsh. But I *saw him*—saw what pain my indulgence could cost him—and I was already filled to overflowing with pain. He was a friend to me—a dear friend, true, but no more. I knew that with him it was different.

"But your pain is mine."

"It should not be so!"

He smiled, and the expression sat lightly on his lean, handsome face. "Who is to say what should and should not be so, Charlotte? A higher wisdom than ours decides that."

"It is wrong to turn to you. It is wrong to burden your kindness."

"It is wrong to refuse what is freely given—freely—with no expectations, no strings attached."

He was right. Who was I to ordain—indeed to meddle, as so many others had? I smiled into his eyes—knowing that my understanding lay in the suffering I saw in his gaze, which, to the soul that bore it, was as great as my own.

CHAPTER EIGHTEEN

ONE THOUGHT ONLY POSSESSED my being and overwhelmed my thoughts. The man I loved was of the same race as my mother; both were Sikhs. My father and I had loved in the same place! And this pathetic realization brought a certain joy to my heart. One cannot explain emotion; emotion often comes unbidden and holds an unwelcome sway. But I allowed myself to believe that if my father were still living, he would understand. His heart would go out to me, and how could he deny me what he himself had once longed for and possessed?

The fact that he was not living, that my life was inexorably altered—I pushed my acute awareness of these realities deep down in my mind, and took comfort from what might have been. Such behavior was foolish, I know. It was a kind of defense against pain—a form of daydreaming that kept some hope alive in my breast, and helped me achieve a resigned serenity as I moved through my days.

In my mind a determination was growing, one I would scarcely admit to. Perhaps after September, when the monsoons had ended and this terrible sickness abated, perhaps then I could go. Only to see him! Only to tell him of my discovery, to share this one last thing with him. So I fancied, allowing desire to have its way with me. For Dr. Fielding had mercifully added, at the end of his letter, than Karan was still living in Calcutta, working in Government House and teaching classes in one of the schools there. I could picture him thus, in a life more truly suited to his nature than soldiering had been. It could do no harm—just to set eyes on him once more, to hear the sound of his voice! So my emotions reasoned, and so I allowed them through the long, rain-soaked days.

Everything suffered from the moisture, even the oil paintings on the wall. Books seemed to crumble in my hands when I touched them, and their covers were glazed over with a fine layer of fungus. The fungus seemed truly a living thing here, growing through each night while we slept, so that the mats were covered with the thick green scum of it every morning and must be scrubbed clean. The servants worked tirelessly to fight back the enemies that assailed on each side. The worst to me were the insects; the very air was alive with them. They settled on everything, soiling food and drink before we could touch it, blackening the curtains and shutters, crawling across the limp covers of my beloved books, pasting themselves along the moist mats that covered floor and wall. They sickened me; I found my appetite waning, and my spirits with it. If it had not been for Winston I most probably would have succumbed and taken to my bed to sleep out the nightmare. But, driven to entertain him, I realized there were still things to do, and ways to drive back the madness that seemed to press in on all sides.

There was one week in August when the rains poured down in torrents for four days in a row. Then five, then six. Then seven. In the mornings the fog was so dense that only the bravest ventured out into it. During the late afternoons the rain would cease for a few precious hours, but the wind refused to be still. I shall never forget the terrible whining, the mournful moan of that wind. The dust it lifted was so dense that we were forced to light candles at midday to find our way. And the eerieness of it, in that cavernous house where the windows rattled and all the doors creaked, ate at me, more than the insects and the mildew together had power to do.

On such afternoons Lieutenant Sheldon came visiting, and he would often bring some of his friends. The sound of normal male voices raised in conversation and laughter helped to dispel the odd sense I had that all life was a dream, gray and gritty, soaked and shivering, a perpetual twilight through which we all moved like so many ghosts.

During that terrible week the nearby river flooded over, submerging every tree in sight, destroying the natives' fields, smashing their huts in its raging brown torrent.

"They take to their boats," Hugh Sheldon assured me, "and ride out the storm, so to speak. Some of us have gone over to assist them." He smiled weakly. "But we have not many to spare."

It was grimly true. Geoffrey came home the evening of the fourth day with news that nearly froze my blood in its veins.

"The colonel, two other majors, and myself stood at muster today," he said. I waited, knowing there was more. "Along with thirty-seven of the men."

"Thirty-seven!" Nearly three hundred had been sent here!

"The rest are in hospital," Geoffrey explained bluntly. "Either dying or dead."

I grabbed his arm. "You must inform the governor-general. It is sheer madness to keep men here, only to kill them like flies!"

He laughed dryly. "The governor-general knows. Is it not madness to keep Englishmen in India at all, my love?"

His eyes seemed unfocused. His laconic manner frightened me more than a tirade of anger would.

"Is there nothing we can do?"

"Do?" His blank eyes stared back at me. "Gentlemen have their means."

I knew what the "gentlemen's means" were. I bit into my lip. "And what if they are not sufficient?"

"Then the gentlemen die. Those of us who are left will walk out of here in October." He shrugged his thin shoulders and laughed again.

"And will you be one of them?" I spat out the words, and their sharpness lifted his head a bit.

"I will be one of them!" he replied through his teeth. "And I will be rich!"

I turned away from him. That last statement weighed on me. There was only one way in India for a minor English officer to make himself rich. I rejected the possibility—I dared not entertain it! I walked down the long hall, in and out of the wavering shadows the oil lanterns made. I felt as if I were bringing a trailing of evil with me from the room I had left. I could feel it, cold at my feet and ankles, scudding along the damp walls. I entered the nursery where Winston waited for me. I sent his ayah away, and we two cuddled close beneath the piled covers and read stories out loud until our eyes burned, then sang ourselves into sleep. But I kept his bodyguard keeping watch outside his closed door, and I had given instructions that one light should be kept burning in the child's room throughout the long night.

The seventh night of the great deluge Geoffrey did not come home at all. I ignored it, knowing his man was with him and he would come to no harm. Nautch girls had been sent for from one of the neighboring villages, "to keep up the men's spirits," as Geoffrey had justified it the last time. These sweet dancing girls, sensuous and alluring in their own fashion, could exert a powerful influence over some men. I felt strangely vulnerable, being in my condition, when I thought of them working their wiles. But in this, as in all things, the circumstances were outside my control. The following night I went to bed at my usual time, which was perhaps later than most—late enough so that my eyes burned and my lids drooped and I could summon that sleep which was the only protection I had from the night and the house—both of which pressed upon me with their darkness, and the dark things they hid. I heard the first sounds, the first shuffling commotion, before a summons could be sent me. I pulled a loose robe around me, which would conceal my growing belly, and awoke Winston's bodyguard, who was a strong, able man. Together we walked the immense length of the hallway, even our slippered feet echoing and our shadows dancing weirdly along the high walls.

I knew before looking. Several of his men had brought Geoffrey home to me. They half-cradled, half carried him, and he was in a stupor of sorts.

"What is it?" I asked the nearest one.

"You do not know the signs?"

I looked up into Hugh Sheldon's solemn face. "Why have you come?" I hissed.

"There were few enough of us standing. I was shanghaied into the party. Do not be ashamed." Even with his voice lowered to little more than a whisper, the sympathy in it sang. "His weakness is no reflection on you! Do not ever dream that it is!"

By this time the men had moved him to the bedroom where they lowered him, with little ceremony, onto the bed. "He'll sleep it off," one of them said.

"He may hallucinate." Lieutenant Sheldon was watching me; I could feel his eyes on my face, gauging my comprehension. "Opium," he said. "Did you not guess it?"

"He is so little home. . . ." My words trailed off; the air about us hung with them. The men began to shuffle their feet, then to file out one by one.

"His boy will be here directly," Hugh Sheldon assured me. "He knows what to do. For your part—avoid him!" He closed his warm hand over my arm. "Think of yourself and . . ." He paused. He must not let his words grow too intimate. The other men were approaching the front door, yet he still lingered.

"By heaven, I hate to leave you, Charlotte! Will you be all right?"

His voice was trembling with his efforts to contain his emotions. "You have made the difference, Hugh. May heaven bless you for your kindness to me."

I had never called him by his given name before. I turned my eyes from the mingling of pain and joy that spread over his face. Then I leaned forward, swaying a little, and pressed my lips to his cheek. "Go now!" I gave him a gentle shove—and when I looked up he was gone.

I, too, left the room, without once looking down at the drugged man whose distorted features bore a marked resemblance to him I called husband—whose child I carried—but who had become a stranger to me.

The days passed. No reference to that night was ever made between us. Indeed, I doubted that Geoffrey even realized I had been there. A week after the incident I received a note, hand carried, from one of Hugh Sheldon's friends, I believe one of the five who had lived in the house with him. Hugh, he informed me, had been in hospital these past four days with the fever.

I thanked the man and gave orders for Cinnamon to be saddled. We rode through the fog at a cautious pace. It had been months since our last ride together. Then, too, my condition was progressing, and I felt awkward and a bit unsure of myself atop his high back. The fog was so thick with moisture that it seemed to chill to the bone, so I entered the hot, crowded hospital with an unanticipated sense of relief. I found the lieutenant's bed only after asking directions half a dozen times. I shrank from looking upon him, remembering that other room and that other bed, and the noble face etched with pain and resentment.

He was sunk in sleep, sunk into the thin mattress as though he were moulded out of it. How thin his cheeks were, how gray his skin in just these few days! There were too many men here—and too few hands to care for them.

I turned away and went in search of an attendant, and gave my instructions to him. I would send my man round and expected Lieutenant Sheldon ready to be released to him.

"This is quite decent of you, ma'am," the young soldier said. "It may indeed prove the means of saving his life."

I agreed, then went in search of my horse and the assistance of the servant to help me up into the saddle. My thoughts were racing ahead of me. The house was so large. I could put him in the unsued wing and assign one of the servants to care for him; I need not do it myself, need not endanger my safety or that of the child I carried.

As soon as I arrived home I hurried about the business of it all, and by midafternoon, the young lieutenant was resting peacefully in the cool, scrubbed room which had been prepared for him. A trusted attendant sat with him. I went about my daily business as though nothing had changed.

For two days we operated thus, with me checking in on my young patient at regular intervals. When one is in a state of perpetual low fever it becomes impossible to eat or drink, sometimes even to sleep. I remembered well how my mouth burned, my head throbbed, and my whole back seemed to be on fire with pain. I knew how he was suffering, yet was encouraged by the care he was receiving; surely that, combined with his youthful constitution, would pull him through.

Not until the third day did I find the opportunity to tell Geoffrey what I had done. He listened, though his eyes at first grew like saucers, then narrowed to slits in his head.

"You are yet presumptuous and spunky, Charlotte," he responded. "Dacca and—all this—have not tamed that out of your system."

He took a strange, perverted pride in my spirit. He liked me better now, when he saw my actions as defying him, than he had during my brief spell of weakness, suffering, and need. His admiration disgusted me, because it was so narrow and insincere, and almost unkind in intent.

"He may stay, ill as he is. But you keep away from him!"

"Keep away from him? Just what do you mean?"

"Stay out of his room, Lottie! Nursing he may have, but not your care and your company. He's already enjoyed plenty of that."

He wanted to imply that things had not been proper between us; but even *he* did not dare that, for he knew how untrue it was, and what sure defenses I would have against any unfounded accusations. I wished very much to return an acid retort: "Well, at least he appreciates my company, which is more than can be said now of you."

But, of course, I did not. I merely answered, "As you like, Geoffrey."

"As I like!" he growled back at me.

"Are any of the sick recovering?" I asked. "Have the numbers at muster increased?"

"Perhaps. A little," he conceded

"Then some few more of us will be able to walk out of here in a month's time," I said, my stomach tightening against his possible responses.

"A month's time!" He snorted. "The wheels of John's Company do not move as efficiently as that."

"It will be a year, come October," I replied, hating the East India Company and the power it had over our lives.

"Yes, but we may have a month or two more than that."

"For what purpose?" I asked. It was the closest I had come to broaching the subject of opium between us. With my eyes I tried to tell him that I was not as naive as he thought. With the whole energy of my soul, with every line of my body I tried to tell him that I was abhorred and disgusted, and could not much longer wink at such behavior as his.

He regarded me thoughtfully, reading much of what I intended. But he did not deign to reply. He could not, without making trouble for himself. Instead he said lightly, "Come now, Lottie. I have granted your request of me. Cannot we two get along?"

Get along? As two polite acquaintances living in the same house? Get along! While he went his way, and expected me to go mine!

I kept my word to Geoffrey and did not go near the sickroom. Winston and I filled our time by playing board games, or building stone forts and towers and then filling them with tiny tin soldiers who, under our direction, massed themselves into lines of battle and were gloriously shot, and just as gloriously resurrected to fight each other again. How simple the world of play that precedes the grimmer realities it so innocently mimes!

Vijaya and I worked on a layette for the baby, and I found myself taking up pen and paper again and sketching, in the harsh strokes of charcoal which seemed especially suited, the scenes of this place, this twilight world where I was sojourning a season. I wondered what lay beyond. But in the dark afternoons, with the rain tearing at the loose shutters and the wind sobbing down the chimneys, such wonderings were dangerous, and could threaten to drive me to madness again. And I allowed myself to think of October, when the monsoons would end and a trip to Calcutta could be made; and this thinking was also a madness of sorts.

Winston had discovered Lieutenant Sheldon by trailing after the servants who attended on him. Something essentially gentle and good within each made them respond to one another, and the child, lonely in a household of adults, sought the older boy's company. I scolded him, then threatened, then punished, but I could not keep him away. The young lieutenant was on the mend, and Winston had already lived through his own bout with the fever, but who was to say he was not susceptible to it still? I worried. I threatened the servants and Winston's ayah, but still the child found opportune moments to slip away. At last I determined to speak to Hugh Sheldon myself.

I had not seen him for weeks, and was delighted at how improved his condition was.

"I shall soon be fit to leave your gracious care," he said. But his eyes bore a mild accusation which I could not ignore.

At last, after promising to send the lad away at once, should he attempt another visit, he gave in to the temptation and asked outright, "Why do you neglect me? Why have you not once come to visit? Do you aid me out of duty only? Has my company lost its savor for you?"

"You know better than that," I said softly.

He was at once ashamed, and penitent, as though he had been the erring one.

"Forgive me for doubting, for having to make sure of what I *knew.*" He leaned forward, his eyes scanning my face anxiously. "Is my presence causing you distress—or trouble—or worse? If so I shall—"

"I am well enough," I answered him. "But you must not think ill of me for my—"

"I could never think ill of you!" he cried. "Nothing under heaven could make me do that!"

Dear boy, I thought. *Why must both you and I be miserable, with no help in this world for either of us?*

I left him as gently as I could, and moved the rest of the day under a cloud of melancholy. The sooty dusk of the afternoon deepened to night. I sat alone, listening to the mosquitoes move against the screens, tuning my ears to hear the scraping of a loose branch along the eaves of the house, which always meant that the wind was rising. I had settled Winston in bed, but I did not feel like going to my own solitary chamber. Geoffrey had not come home. But if he were here, what real difference would that make?

At last I rose heavily and walked the long corridor to my bedroom, where Vijaya was waiting to assist me.

"I feel young and restless tonight," I told her, "despite the child that I carry."

"You carry this one well," she responded, ignoring the dangerous part of my comment. "You are halfway through your term, yet one would not know it by your presence and carriage."

"Good. Perhaps at last I am learning something from you." I sat on the edge of the bed and began to uncoil my long braid.

"Let me do that," she protested as Shadow scurried up the bedclothes and wrapped himself round my shoulders. I scratched him along the cheekbone and then stroked his smooth fur.

"I *am* young!" I said. "Here I am smothered by life, as well as forsaken. I wish I—"

With a hissing whisper Vijaya pressed her finger against my lips. "It is bad luck to speak one's wishes aloud," she warned, "especially in a place such as this. The evil here would suck up all of your wishes and then laugh at your pain."

I looked at her face. She meant every word she was saying

I could not dismiss her words; they settled like stones on my heart.

I crawled into bed, but I could not sleep, so I lit a lamp and read for a while. At length I heard sounds in the distance and surmised that Geoffrey had arrived, and the hour was not too abominable. Perhaps I would go out and greet him. Perhaps some civility between us . . .

I put on robe and slippers and walked out into the hall where the lights hissed and gusts of cool air swirled round my feet. Geoffrey was standing in the front entry. He turned sharply and saw me, so I lifted my hand in a greeting. But in long strides he cleared the distance between us and stood glowering down upon me.

"What are you doing here—now?"

I thought it a strange question. I knew it masked something, perhaps something evil he wished to hide. I saw in the shadows behind Geoffrey a dark figure bend over and attempt to conceal itself as it stole toward the darkened sitting room. I recognized the figure.

"What are you doing away from your post, Jimmund?" I demanded. "You should be tending to the young lieutenant, and I do not remember dismissing you."

Jimmund froze. The air hummed with his guilt, like a string drawn too taut. Then, all of a sudden, I knew. I turned on my heel and strode down the long, unlit corridor to where the sickroom had been. The shadows grew deeper. My feet threatened to stumble, and I had to clench my hands at my sides to keep from throwing them out in front of me, groping for sight and direction. But knowing that my husband watched me, I struggled on.

"You will not find him there!" Geoffrey bellowed from behind me.

This time I turned around slowly. "What have you done?" I began to retrace my way, heaviness dragging at each step.

"Sent the lad packing!" There was obvious triumph in his tone.

"And why have you done that?"

"You know why. It is *your doing,* Charlotte."

I could not keep from wincing at his cruelty. Slowly his meaning, twisted as it was, began to come through to me.

"You did not keep your word." He spoke to me in a tone he might use with an errant child who was threatened with punishment.

I bit hard against my lip. "I kept my word to you, save one time only," I replied. "And that one time was in an attempt to protect Winston from harm."

"Whatever are you talking about?"

I was approaching him closely now, and kept walking, so that he backed a few steps away from me.

"Jimmund did not report that?" I glanced over at the cowering servant, fighting against the sickness that rose in my stomach at the thought of his petty perfidy.

In a few terse words I explained the situation to Geoffrey, planning, as I spoke, my next move; for I knew I must move fast, follow up this slight advantage that had been vouchsafed me.

"Where is the lieutenant now?" I demanded.

"Finding his way down the hill, I imagine," Geoffrey answered, dropping his slightly confused gaze from mine.

"You drove him out into the night—in this weather—to walk to his death!"

I turned and called through the echoing hall for Yusaf. "I will send a servant I can trust to retrieve him."

"You will do no such thing, Lottie!"

I whirled back on Geoffrey, my eyes blazing, no longer trying to contain my ire. "Would you rather I not—and let you be known as a cold-blooded murderer? For such you would be."

His eyes went as pale as his face. Something within him seemed to retreat from me, and I sensed it. "Jimmund," I barked, not even turning about to face the man. "You and all yours will be gone before sunrise, and the wrath of Kali will visit you if I ever catch sight of you near this place."

He hesitated. I could feel his shivering. "Now! At once! Or I shall fetch the big one to aid you."

"The big one" was Winston's bodyguard, who, it was well known, was devoted to me.

Jimmund moved. I held my breath, every second expecting Geoffrey to countermand me. But he did not speak. I fetched two of the housemaids and set them to lighting lamps and righting the sickroom again. Geoffrey stood watching me. When all had been done that could be done, I turned to face him again.

"I shall still keep to the conditions you set regarding the lieutenant's presence here—and willingly," I added. "Save that tomorrow morning I shall check once to see that the invalid fares well and is being cared for according to my instructions." We stood facing each other, his shame like a barrier between us. I did not need to hurl accusations at him; they were well spoken without words.

"I am going back to bed now," I announced, and began the long walk down the dim passage. I had been strong—I had felt strength beyond my expectations flow through me. I should have been glad. I had won—I had averted disgrace and catastrophe. But I knew, even through my anger and my weariness, that it was an empty victory at best.

Chapter Nineteen

THE RAINS CEASED. THE RIVER receded and flowed with docile regularity through its proper channel. The natives began to clean, restore, replant, according to ancient custom. The time for leaving had come.

Geoffrey would hear none of it. His orders came from the governor-general, and he had not yet received them. I sensed more deeply than ever that my husband had an agenda of his own. Very well. His stubbornness could serve my purposes, too. I began making plans to travel down the river to Calcutta.

Once the decision was finalized in my mind, all fear and hesitation passed from me. My only concern was how Winston would fare in my absence. Otherwise, I felt quite at peace. I had at last released Lieutenant Sheldon from sick quarters with a clean bill of health, and I felt the whole experience represented a triumph of spirit over all that was dross and deficient in life. The young man would make a fair contribution to society, and in all probability live a full, worthwhile life. He was well worth the saving—well worth the trouble.

Hope came on the breath of October's cool breezes. Perhaps I would spend my birthday in the city—perhaps I should even on that day be in the company of—I had to stop myself from anticipations which would make *any* reality prove lusterless by comparison. Vijaya would travel with me, and one of the officer's wives whose brother was stationed in

Calcutta and who had kindly agreed to accommodate us during our stay there. Her bodyguard and three other servants would also accompany us. All our plans were in order, save the last painful necessity of informing my husband of what was about to take place. This fearsome task lay like a weight on my heart—sat like a black cloud above my head during all my waking hours. But the terrible anxiety it caused me, like the hope that was almost as terrible, was, in the end, all in vain.

Geoffrey came home one evening two or three hours earlier than was his custom and took to his bed. I suspected nothing and left him to the care of his boy, as usual. But the following morning he did not rise. He had not stirred from his bed by midday, so I sought out his servant, even yet believing that he must be sleeping off a particularly active bout of drinking the night before.

The man pointed to his own head. "Fever—head very hot and on fire."

"Have you sent for the doctor?" I asked.

"Sahib refuses—will not allow it."

Then perhaps his illness *did* have something to do with misbehavior, perhaps with the use of the dreaded opium—which terror I usually managed to avoid thinking about altogether. Perhaps it was best to let sleeping dogs lie. I tiptoed in to check on him once in the late afternoon, but he slept soundly, under a pile of blankets, and in the darkened room, I could make out very little.

The following day I questioned his boy several times, but his answers were so evasive that I at last went to see for myself. My husband was in an advanced stage of brain fever, and the look of him frightened me. I scribbled a note on a scrap of brown native paper and sent it by means of our fastest runner, urging the regimental doctor to come at once. The air hung heavy, the servants muffling their voices and even the sounds of their labor as we waited. Tragedy and superstition go hand in hand with these people, and the effects of this "haunted house" was not lost on them, nor, for that matter, their master's erratic, unusually malicious behavior since our arrival here.

The doctor came, and stayed closeted a long time in the sickroom. When he came out he called me aside. "Your husband is dangerously ill," he informed me. "Have you not known?"

"I have not," I responded, disliking the clear implications behind his words and tone. "But I am prepared to do whatever may be required of me."

He lifted an appraising eyebrow, unpersuaded as he took in my state.

"You will need help," he pronounced bluntly. "Medication must be administered to him—carefully, without error or delay—every two hours, all day and all night. That alone . . ." His gaze grew more rueful. "I shall dispatch two officers to assist you; they can spell one another."

I nodded, but refused to thank him. In addition to his curt ways, he had uncaring eyes. *He is not a healer, like Dr. Fielding,* I thought to myself.

"Your husband is a drinker—a heavy user of alcohol, is he not, Mrs. Hillard?"

I nodded again.

"It would go better with him if he were not."

He spoke the words like a death knell, and for the first time a cold shudder shook through my frame.

"I will check back tomorrow." The doctor straightened his hat and shirt collar. "Pray as you watch, ma'am," he said. "Yes, if you are a praying woman, I would strongly advise you to pray as you watch."

Pray. Pray for what? Perhaps there are "praying women," as the doctor termed it, but I had never known any. Did Sita Beg pray? When the handsome, laughing Englishman fell in love with her, did she pray to one of her gods in gratitude for the favor? No. She had been a Sikh; Sikhs pray to one god only. One god who had not the power to return her to her husband and child, despite the years and years of anguished prayers she must have raised to him. May all the gods forgive me, but during those first hours, I prayed more for myself and the gentle man who was once again lost to me than I did for him who hovered, unaware, on that solemn line between life and death.

For ten days Geoffrey was expected to die momentarily, and I watched by his bed day and night, with Shadow curled up in a warm brown coil in my lap. Vijaya was not happy, but since she could not dissuade me, she turned her attentions to Winston, which pleased me well. The assigned officers dozed more frequently at their posts than I did, waking chagrined when I had already administered the medication without their aid.

After four days I sent word by Vijaya to Colonel May's wife, explaining the situation and expressing my deep regret and disappointment at not being able to make the proposed journey with her. I took one more liberty, too. I wrote a letter to Karan, addressing it to Government House, and asking her kind indulgence in having one of her servants deliver it once she arrived safely there. Vijaya said nothing when she took it from my hand, but her eyes spoke volumes which I refused to let myself read. That ended it, after all. Ended everything. What objections could she possibly have?

I sat in the unquiet house, heavy with so many burdens from lives that had now whispered themselves away into dust. I felt the desolation, the hopelessness, and wondered if my husband would die. On the eleventh day the doctor pronounced that there was now some little hope, though he certainly was not yet out of danger. I left Geoffrey in the care of the soldiers and went into my own room and cried. Then I lay in the cool, solitary comfort of that chamber and slept. I slept for a day and a night, and part of another day. When I awoke I learned that Geoffrey was still steadily improving, and if this continued, we ought to be able to expect him to live. He had taken nearly five hundred grains of calomel before his system was salinated, whereas the normal doses were from one half to five grains. Extreme measures, and he had survived them. Five days later Colonel May came by in person to inform me that as soon as Geoffrey was strong enough to be moved, he would receive his new orders: he was to be sent back to England.

I must have blinked stupidly at him.

"It will be a pleasing change for you, Mrs. Hillard," he encouraged me. "Geoffrey will need a good long rest after his bout. Besides, he's near time for a leave, as it is."

Every few years, I knew, the men were allowed a year's time off-duty to return home, if they liked. Many were unable to take advantage of what seemed a generous system, since travel expenses and living expenses while in England had to come from their own purse. During my years with them, Major Reid and Constance had never returned.

I felt Colonel May patting my shoulder in a fatherly manner. "You take care of yourself, lass, you hear? The servants can nurse that rascal husband of yours."

A kind man, covering his gentleness with bluster, as so many in the service do. I thanked him. I called a servant to see him out. *England.* I sank into the nearest chair. I had never wanted to go there, even when my curiosity was roused by the boys' returning to school. India was home. England was thousands of miles from here—from all that I knew and loved.

If I am wrenched away from this place, I shall never return, a voice said inside me. And the voice was not a whisper, but more of a sob. And the black surety of the voice seemed to mock and taunt me from every dusty corner, from every shadowy nook and echoing chamber of that dark, abominable house.

The orders were wise. Geoffrey recovered, but he remained in many ways weak; *broken* was the word which came to my mind. At first he raved against the orders, snarling at me as though I were responsible for them. But the colonel must have spoken to him. And after grudging acceptance came resignation, then a kind of delight, a twisted anticipation of what advantage he might turn for himself back in merry old England. None of what might have come earlier, talk of the kind of life we could make together, talk of children and home. He was yet bound too tightly to his own secret practices and ambitions.

At last, unable to help myself, I said to him one day, "I am afraid, Geoffrey. Afraid to travel in this state. Afraid for Winston's safety. Afraid of what England will be like once we get there."

"You will do well enough," he rejoined. "You've strength and spirit sufficient to weather the passage. And you'll make a great hit in England, with your honey-smooth skin and your provocative brown eyes. That is, if you don't let the green storm lights flash too often."

Despite the implied rebuke in his last words, he had meant his reply as a compliment; I could tell that he had. It warmed me; even this little bit warmed me and lent me pluck to go on.

"I do not wish to leave India. This is my home. I never intended to live elsewhere."

"Then you should not have married an Englishman."

Of course, he was right. His words brought me back sharply to those terrible days when my decision had been made for me. Youth has not the wisdom to look ahead. Yet what would foresight have given me, or how would it have altered my fate?

We began to prepare, selling for what I thought a pittance the countless items we could not take with us. I watched my whole life, spread out before me, being parceled off piece by piece. We packed many a *pitara,* sturdy cane boxes lined inside with tin sheets. These carried our clothing and the selection of books I was allowed to bring with us, and little more—a few trinkets, some of Winston's most prized playthings.

"Will we come back here, Mama?" he asked.

"To this place or to India?" I replied, stalling a little.

"I know you will not come back here!" He wrinkled his nose in distaste, unconsciously mimicking my expression. "But India?"

I avoided the searching gaze of the blue eyes. I would not lie to him; I had never yet lied to him. "I do not believe we shall ever return."

"What if we wish to? What if we don't like England?"

"We shall *try* to like it, and therefore we shall, Winston!"

"Do you really think that we can?"

"We must!" I smiled, but my lips went all twisted. "We shall have each other, remember? That will make anything right."

He could hear the tears in my voice. I knew he saw through my heroics, as perhaps most children cannot. He slipped his hand into mine, as he had so often in the early days, nearly undoing me with his tenderness and concern.

I wrote to Alan Fielding, such an unsatisfactory method of saying good-bye. I tried to do as before—pretend he was standing beside me, his narrow frame bent slightly forward in a listening attitude. I tried to tell him the thoughts of my heart, feeling very much like a person who has had the sentence of death passed upon him and is making his peace with the world. But for some things there can be no peace. I was leaving behind the mother who still was lost to me. In the dark house at Dacca I had allowed myself to fantasize of the day when I would discover her—perhaps place ads in the newspapers, contrive a reward, some enticement to bring her captors forward. After all, what risk was there now? My father was long since dead; I a grown woman, with no claims on her. But to know of her safety—to see her just once, face to face! Was this not to be? Was I to embark into the wide world with this unresolved horror still heavy upon me?

I put forward few requests, but I wanted Vijaya to come with me. Geoffrey nearly laughed out loud when I told him.

"Have you gone mad on me again, Lottie? Nothing in the world could induce me to take that woman to England with me."

"I need a servant, especially in my present condition."

"Radha can care for both you and the lad. We'll find English nannies for both him and the child after we get there." England, fix all, where every condition would be perfect. It made me a little bit ill.

"Passage is costly," he reminded me, knowing he had an unassailable point there. "Besides, these people have no desire to leave their homeland, especially with someone who will not return!"

I held my peace; I would ask no more favors of him. Later that evening, when we were alone together, Vijaya approached me in that measured, quiet way of hers.

"Sahib is right," she said. "If you won your case for me, still I would not go."

You would leave me! You would expect me to face the world without you! I wanted to shout at her, but I bit my tongue on the words.

"I am too old to leave the land of my father's and die a stranger's death," she said. "You know this to be true."

I opened my mouth, but she silenced me with a gesture. "I have loved you truly; take that knowledge with you."

Her words sunk deep, like round coins of pure sunlight seeping right through my chilled skin. She *had* loved me and sacrificed more than I could imagine in coming back into this house for my sake.

"Make your mind up to it," she said. "You are only what you carry inside." A sweet, reserved smile played at the corners of her full mouth. "And since you will carry my devotion with you as long as life breathes through your veins—ah, see how much, indeed, you shall be."

Dr. Fielding had spoken much the same words concerning the friendship we shared, the kindred spirits we were. And Karan—Karan had said thus of the spirits of my mother and me.

"My heart is slow to learn," I muttered.

"Because it is slow to *believe,*" Vijaya said, and I knew she spoke true.

We were to travel by river to Calcutta where, after several days' time, our ship would sail. We arrived without incident after nearly a month of grueling travel which, in India, is considered as nothing at all. At least we were safe. I had even rested from time to time along the dull stretches, trying to remind myself that this was the last I would see of my country: the last ill-clad beggars, the last starving villagers camping by river and stream, the last unwanted children sold to the highest bidder and used at his pleasure, the last human nightmares.

But, of course, there was more. There were the sunsets, filtering like a red glaze over the desert; there were the wonderful flowers and the even more colorful birds; the lumbering but somehow graceful elephants, filling the quiet air with their cries; and there were the countless temples and mosques and monuments that dotted the land, mute witnesses to races of men who had passed into memory and were no more, but whose throbbing souls helped make up the white dust of India and of India's dream.

I thought the city an ugly place, with very much of the English about it. I knew it was named *Kalikata*—spot where the little toe of Kali landed when Vishnu the Preserver cut her corpse into fifty-two pieces and flung them over the face of the earth, to stop her husband's wild and raging grieving at her death. Very Hindu. But the edges and intersections of the roads are lined with British statues: the king and the great lords who served him. The street fronts themselves are a confusing array of every sort of architecture, from wooden blinds and iron balconies and wires with wash hanging down, to doorways framed by Doric columns whose windows, a storey above, are carved in a faintly Mogul style. And then the rooftops—these, too, are lined with monuments, from horses and lions rampant, to naked young ladies and feathered hawks swooping down. No form, no order, only a mad mixing of cultures half-crazed, half-ruined, half-begun.

Geoffrey had business during our brief stay, and he had forbidden me to as much as step out of the house where we were quartered. The bazaars were forbidden to me, as were the spots of interest to a visiting tourist. He was not well yet himself, and spent only short periods away at any one time so that his comings and goings were erratic and hard to judge. I did not have the heart and energy to oppose him. Government House is a large place, and I would be recognized there, stopped and questioned, with assistance offered me. I could not merely walk in and inquire after the whereabouts of a lowly native employee. I had accepted that fact. I had accepted the fact that this city was to be my last stage of torment, my last test of endurance before I embarked into the unknown and left India forever behind.

I felt him. Some will scoff and discredit my words altogether. But I felt his presence before I opened the door to him. When I saw Karan standing before me, supple and warm fleshed, his golden eyes moving over me, I became suddenly weak and light-headed and had to lean against the door frame in order to stand. He put out a hand to steady me. That precious touch of his fingers, even through the fabric of my sleeve!

"Charlotte, Charlotte, Charlotte!" He kept repeating the word of my name like a prayer. But to me it had the sound of music when formed in his mouth.

"I have stunned you, and caused you—too much pain."

"Pain cannot be avoided in a meeting like this."

He smiled slowly. He was in good trim and walked with only a slight limp as he moved to a chair. A snowy turban still framed his solemn and finely drawn face.

"Sit down, Charlotte. It pains me to see you so pale, and so—"

"Unhappy?" I said.

"Adversity has only deepened the impress of God's mark on your features," he replied as his eyes searched my face. "You are, I fear, lovelier than the last time I saw you."

I sat down across from him. "How is Government House?"

"A mass of confusion and graft; has not government ever been thus? But I am earning respect in my own small sphere."

"I do not doubt it," I said. "Is the work challenging?"

"Not the work, but the teaching. The teaching gives some threshold on which my spirit can function as well as my mind."

"I am glad of it. Will you stay?"

"For the time being. Probably forever. I am too spoiled by the ways of the English to be able to return with content to the villager's life."

"That is not all bad," I argued. "The education you have received is not all bad."

He meant to resist, to disagree for the sake of a fine and intelligent argument. But, seeming to remember where he was and with whom he was speaking, he altered his intent. "Of course not; you are right. I have been exposed to the best of another culture as well as the worst of it, and am the wiser because of it. So you are to return, to find out what the English side of you is truly about."

"How do you know this? How did you discover me?"

"There is a bit of a story to that." He leaned forward in anticipation of his own words. "Several nights ago I dreamed of you—a strange, vivid dream. The following day two men who work near me had been discussing how their friend, Major Hillard, had been dangerously ill; had been, indeed, on the edge of death; and now he was being sent home. I questioned them, stretching my own connections—or, perhaps I should say misrepresenting them."

It was torment to be so near to him, and to know he was lost to me still!

"Let me stay with you," I cried. "If I go to England I will be as some exotic flower, uprooted, torn from its native soil, destined to wither and die."

He shook his head at me; fine creases of worry lined his forehead. "Do not do this, Charlotte."

"I cannot be torn away from you," I said bluntly, "and hope to survive."

Vijaya's wise words whispered in my head, but I pushed their echo aside. I would have him, if such a chance existed. I would grasp at any straws now!

"Let me stay with you."

"It would never be permitted, Charlotte—it would not be *endured!* Do you understand what I am saying?"

I understood only too well. I hung my head, shorn of defense, stripped of argument. Yet his searing words had masked no anger, carried no sting of accusation. They had been spoken in sorrow, in the most kindly sorrow.

"Then why have you come?" I asked. "To drive me over the brink of madness and despair?"

He said nothing for a few moments, sitting silent and passive, his eyes staring hard at the floor. "I have come to remind you of my pledge of love to you," he said. "And, yes, in my weakness, to feast my eyes upon you once more—"

With a little cry I rose from my chair and turned from him.

"Forgive me, Charlotte," he said.

"There is nothing to forgive. The joy is worth the anguish. I would have wished it no other way."

"Besides," he went on after a moment. "I have not yet told you my dream."

"Your dream?"

"Yes. You see, in my dream I saw you—saw you in a place other than India. But I did not know—I did not suspect yet the change that was in store for you."

"And in your dream, where did you see me?"

"I saw you in a country that was strangely much like our own. A land of deserts that was barren and treeless, a great empty basin bounded on the east by high, snow-crowned mountains, and set off in the west by a lower range and a sprawling blue lake."

"You saw this distinctly."

He nodded. "Quite distinctly."

"It does not sound like England to me. What was I doing in your dream?"

"Nothing that I can remember."

I raised my eyebrows a little, but his manner remained unruffled.

"I do not care what you say, or even what you think, Charlotte. I saw what I saw. And I knew, as I looked upon you, that you were where you belonged!"

The words clung to me, unwanted; I would have brushed them away from me.

"You were where you belonged; that was the one thought that stayed with me, even when I awoke."

"Very well. I shall go in peace." I was angry.

"With my blessing," he said. "With the love which I shall keep bright and polished as a jewel, which shall never grow dim whilst I live!"

Useless to me! I wanted to cry. But that would wound him

too deeply. I was young. Life had cheated me. I wanted the warm reality of him, not love's ideal, which was as far and dim a star to follow as faith.

"My beloved," he whispered, "please forgive me for leaving you—for being powerless to deliver you!"

I could feel him yearning toward me. I could feel the force of his pain. I moved, and in a moment was beside him, was encircled once more in his arms—whole in the unity of spirit that knows not man's bounds, but dwells where pain cannot go, nor doubt, nor loss, nor separation.

Let it be enough! my heart begged. *Let it be enough to last me a lifetime. Let the blessing of this moment never leave me, never fade or grow dim.*

Thus I prayed, in the fastness of my spirit, and felt a benediction I could not explain settle over my soul, and weave cords of peace between us—a peace nearly as deep as our love.

Chapter Twenty

SHIPBOARD LIFE CONTRIVED TO be an extension of English society: card games and dancing in the evening, and tea as regular as clockwork. At first I was inclined to believe that they might really succeed, though I much preferred listening to the sailors on deck singing in harmony together the songs of love and longing and parting from half a dozen different nations, and sometimes in more than one tongue. I do not fear water, and the sea air was invigorating. I took one day at a time, and when I felt ill, I ignored it, plying myself with one of Vijaya's many remedies which she had sent along, and leaving Winston for a while exclusively in Radha's care. Geoffrey still had his boy to attend him, and in truth he required him, for he was not strong and fit yet, and spent more time than he wanted stretched out in his cabin, resting.

"I have not been home for over fifteen years," he told me one morning while we walked the smooth deck together. "I wonder if anyone will even remember me."

"What of your family?" I asked. In India the importance of family, of connections back in England, become deflated; of what value are such things there? India is her own world, and even the Englishman's standards adjust and alter for her, at least where they must.

"I have very little. My parents died when I was in my twenties, which is partially why I went into the service, my father being a younger son and not standing to inherit anything anyway." He grimaced, obviously at the memories his words were stirring. "My elderly uncle holds the property, and I have a maiden aunt living somewhere in London."

"And we are headed for London?"

"We are. I have some few investments there."

"Would not living in the country be less costly?" I had been speaking with some of the other women and listening to their conversations, but the places they spoke of were only words to me, with no images behind them at all.

"For us it would not."

I knew there were opium dens in the city, and opium trade there. What would happen to us?

This is my own I return to, I told myself over and over again. *I am an Englishwoman. This blood in my veins entitles me!* Entitled me to what? To fit in, be accepted, be happy? None of those vital factors was within my control. I was a sojourner. Perhaps I would remain a sojourner for the rest of my life.

After weeks of fine days and calm seas we came in for bad weather, with contrary winds and heavy gales. These gales blew every Sunday for six consecutive weeks, and for over a month we ate sea pie, which is a dish composed of lumps of pasta mixed with meat and potatoes, all cooked into a sort of stew, which will swing safe in a large cauldron, like a witch's brew, when the seas are too rough.

We saw very little of the other passengers, for everyone kept to their cabins. I forced the wretched food down me, sometimes holding my nose tight so as to get down the worst of it, for the sake of my child. The captain had veered far south, to where the whalers ply their trade, and after one of the worst storms we saw a sailor's straw hat floating, just bobbing along nicely on the top of the sea. But shortly after, the body of the poor man surfaced also. He had been only a lad, not older than twenty, I would judge. To some he appeared a bad omen, but I was not concerned with such things. I knew the child I carried was destined to be born on this vessel, for good or for ill. A competent doctor traveled with us, as well as an experienced midwife.

No place could be worse than Dacca, I thought to myself. *The ocean water cleanses all evil, and man is close to the elements here. If this child is meant to live, it will live, and the sea winds will caress it, and the gods of the deep call it good.*

So I reasoned, refusing to let anxiety claim me. But then the hurricane struck, and I wondered if all of us were meant to perish by storm and go down to a watery grave.

It came on so quickly that Geoffrey scarcely had time to drag Winston from the passageway, where he was playing with some of the other children, into the cabin itself. He had to brace himself with one foot on the floor and the other on the side of the wall. Radha managed to follow him, calling out to the other servants. The captain had come down to look at the barometer, and his face went ashen when he saw it.

"We are all doomed," he told Geoffrey. "I can do nothing more to save her."

When we were all gathered, huddling pathetically together, Geoffrey closed the door to the cabin and stated, with his soldier's cryptic efficiency, "The captain despairs of saving the vessel. We must all prepare to die together."

With the calm and courage of his soldier's training, he remained composed and resigned, even comforting the wide-eyed and frightened servants. I hugged Winston close to my side. He was crying softly. "I do not wish to die, Mother."

"If it is God's will, then we must, and he will help us, my dearest."

The vessel took a great lurch which brought her to the verge of capsizing. We could feel the violent trembling as the ship tried to right herself—*like a great, living beast,* I thought, *as frightened and helpless as we are.* Then she suddenly lurched to the other side, where she lay spent and trembling again. The timbers cracked, and it sounded as if the whole ship were tearing to pieces around us. *Now,* I thought, *now we will feel it. The shock of cold water closing over us. Are we to meet God? Are we to learn the great secret?*

But the vessel righted herself. By some power which even the seamen could not answer for, she righted her trembling timbers and flew before the black storm, determined to weather the mountains of waves that still could crush her and plunge us all to our deaths.

Life is so dear, I thought. *God has granted each of us, cowering before his great powers, another chance.* And if anything on our journey was to be thought of as an omen, I considered it this.

The child came easily. There was none of the black terror and the even blacker pain I remembered from the last time, when my poor babe had been torn from me. Though all my muscles were weak with the strain and the effort, though the pain was like a searing fire within me—yet it could be endured. And after what seemed like a short while it was over, and my own daughter lay breathing against me. And then I wept.

"It is the exhaustion," the doctor said.

But I looked into the misted eyes of the midwife and said to her, "No, it is the joy."

They left us alone, and I gazed into infant eyes that appeared as unlighted pools—blank and sightless, they say. I do not believe it. In their depths they reflect the eternities from which they have come. How could anyone hold a newborn infant in his arms and deny the existence of God? I saw, with some sort of a spiritual vision, I felt with my heart unspoken truths that had never been explained or revealed to me.

"I would like to come to know God someday," I said out loud to her. I brushed my finger along her curved, silken cheek. "To thank him for you, properly," I whispered. "To understand what it is that I see in your gaze."

When we docked at London we had been over four months on board the ship. I had turned twenty years old before leaving India; Winston was a great boy of six. The child Radha carried, wrapped and bundled in her arms, was nearly two months old

Geoffrey was pleased with her. She was not the son he had wanted, but she was so much more delightful, and posed no threat at all. And she *was* beautiful to look upon: thick auburn hair that tickled her neckline and curled on her cheeks; big, deep-set eyes that would never be blue like Winston's; a mouth and ears that were well moulded—every detail formed to perfection. And she had the disposition of an angel.

"It is the ocean breezes," I said. "She is used to their lullaby and to the gentle rocking of the waters. How in the world will we keep her happy once we get her on land?"

"You may name her," Geoffrey had said shortly after he first set eyes on her and was under the spell of her birth.

"I like your mother's name," I replied, and I meant it. "She must bear a good English name. Sarah, for your mother, and Elizabeth, for my father's mother."

"So be it," he pronounced, not knowing what to make of me.

"But I shall still call you my little Sita whenever it pleases me," I whispered to my daughter. For her most noble blood came from the Sikh princess who had risked safety and station to preserve the life of her child.

Mata, Mata! I cried in my heart. *I would sacrifice three lifetimes to share this moment with you.*

But God speaks, or karma, and the world turns round to its own tune, not to any desires of ours. We do what we can, day following day, and that is all there is to it. But I had my child! A daughter. Flesh of my flesh, binding my mother to me.

London. The heart of England since before the Romans set foot on their soil. London, the city of cities, where men gather for profit, for comfort, for entertainment; where daily, lives and fortunes are bought and sold.

The air was thick with it, the smell and taste of humanity—humanity moving and thriving, climbing over each other's backs to rise a little higher. Yes, there was poverty here. But the ignorance and hopelessness of India was not present, or at least I did not see it at first.

Geoffrey loved it. It worked like a tonic on his senses. He had arrived with money in his pockets, and he found us a good house in Southsea, where he had Indian friends.

April was just pushing out the last gray days of winter, and there was the taste of hope in the air.

"You will grow better," I told Geoffrey. "The air is so clean here."

"London air, clean!" he scoffed. "We must take you to the country."

I smiled. There was more kind indulgence in his tone than I had heard for a year.

I had brought my little flying squirrel with me, and he had survived, weak and wasted like the rest of us, but still eating fruit from my hand. He was India to me, but so was Winston.

"You are my India child," I told him.

"And Sarah?"

"Sarah is a white bird in flight that links our two worlds."

He liked that. "And we will have an England child?"

"Yes, that might be nice."

He cared for the frightened creature, as he had aboard ship, while I cared for the baby. It helped us both settle in. Radha had agreed to stay three months with us, but we must secure a new staff, hire strangers whose ways would be so different from our ways.

The wives of the Indian officers were, of course, full of advice. I tried to listen, I tried to trust what they told me. But their hearts were not my heart, and most had been back in England for some time—England which had been home to them before their years of exile in India. It was different with me. They knew it, but they chose to ignore it. They were extending me *grace.* If I were wise enough to adapt, to become *like them,* then, in their kindness, they would bend the rules a bit and welcome me in. After all, I was a major's wife, despite the dark hue of my skin. The camaraderie of the elite could be stretched to extend to me if I obeyed all the rules. I knew this as clearly as if they had said it. But I did not know where to begin, or even how to do what they expected of me.

Geoffrey took over and made most of the decisions concerning the servants, and perhaps that was well. I knew nothing of the nature of the English serving class and the types of positions which existed here. But one thing I learned at the offset: there were to be far, far fewer servants here. An English matron took an active hand in running her household, and I was grateful for that. No languishing in the heat, or chafing in inaction during the monsoon season. Here life went on as usual, no matter what time of the year. I thought I would like that. But servants were certainly more expensive, and Geoffrey was spending large sums of money with very little concern.

When I questioned him about it, he snorted in impatience. "I have my affairs well in hand, Charlotte."

"They are my affairs, too. I have a right to know of them, to have a hand in decisions that affect my own life."

My words did not please him; he considered them too presumptuous. "I take care of you, I pay the bills and keep things running. That is all you need to know."

I did not agree with him, but it would do no good to argue. He had worked out a household budget, and the running of this one area, servants included, was left entirely to me. I began cutting corners, shopping the Covent Garden markets myself, in search of bargains, scolding the cook for extravagance if she cooked an excess of food which would end up being thrown away. I found a slightly inferior grade of candles which could be bought cheaply in bulk, and yet burned well, with no smoking. I lit no fires in the empty rooms that sat unused day after day. I instructed that the scullery maid be sent to St. Giles, where the costermongers sold fish at a fraction of the price found in regular markets. In this manner I saved a few pennies here and there, and carefully tucked them away. I could not have said what drove me to do this exactly, but it made me feel good, and I took pride in the sharp sense of thrift I was developing.

Our second week in London I posted a letter to Constance at her sister's address. It was a hard thing to do, and caused me much uncertainty and vexation. It was my love for the boys that drove me, and my enduring interest in Lucinda Jane and what had become of her, growing up—as my own daughter would—a thoroughly English child.

I did not expect a reply; I hardly hoped for one. But in very short order, an envelope was put into my hand. I opened it alone, in the front sitting room where the warm yellow walls and chintz-covered furniture might cheer me. Why was I so superstitious that I had to fear what it would say?

As I unfolded the pages I realized that the hand was a young one, the letters uneven and hastily formed. "Dearest Lottie," it began, "I am writing in place of Mama who has been ill these past months and will speak or write to no one. Auntie said that I might."

How like Constance. She had not changed. Why had I fancied she might? This was Arthur; it must be Arthur!

"Hugh and I miss you awfully," the next sentence read. My heart jumped. Suddenly they were real again, as they had not been to me these past years. "But do not think of us as the boys we were when we left you. We are both quite grown up."

He went on for a bit, telling of school honors and achievements and their youthful plans for the future. I was not prepared for the sudden revelation that struck with such cruel force.

"The wretched news is that our Lucy died this past winter." I stared at the words, unwilling to accept the truth of them. "Mother went quite to pieces, Aunt has had the deuce of a time with her, and it has been most dreadful for all."

British understatement. But I grimaced at the outrageous scenes and black sufferings his plucky words masked.

I must go to them, I thought, my heart drawn out in sympathy, even to her. But Arthur's next words checked me.

"We all leave Thursday next for the south of France, where it is hoped that Mother might find some peace."

It is hoped—by whom? Would France prove only a sorrowful prison, ruled by the tyranny of Constance's suffering, as Simla had been?

"I have no address as yet to which you might direct your responses, but I shall keep in touch, Lottie. I believe a visit from you would do Mama good. And it would be jolly fun for Hugh and me to see you! But you are right here in England now, and so we shall see one another, shan't we? This is not India. Distances here are so shrunken. It will be no trouble at all."

He went on for a bit before signing his name with a flourish. *Poor lad,* I thought. *He must not know of the falling out that has taken place between myself and his parents. Irreparable then, and possibly more so now.* In my newsy chattering I had told Constance of the birth of my own daughter, and she would never be able to abide that after the loss of her own. That I should be handed such happiness after the painful, almost unthinkable sacrifices she had made to secure hers! Now all was in vain. God disposes, not man. Her selfish concentration had not really altered her fate. But, oh, it was a hard fate, even to my way of thinking, even for such as herself.

There were crows in England, as raucous and quarrelsome as the ones in India had been. They were one sight and sound I could recognize with a sense of the familiar. But most of the sounds of the city were new and strange to my ears. Thousands of wagons, cabs, and coaches passed by on the streets, with the rattle of wheels and the heavy clop-clop of the horses' feet a constant undercurrent below all other sounds. The cries of peddlers of all types and varieties pierced the thin air with dozens of discordant notes. Even the nights were not still, for the horses and coaches passed even then—lights wavering, drivers calling out to the weary beasts. And the staggering streetwalkers sang in unison together, like troupes of gypsy performers whom even the midnight shadows could not keep still.

Much of the night life of London centered around her many theatres and the elite clubs which had sprung up for this or that sort of men. Geoffrey went almost nightly to some affair or another, often restricted to gentlemen only. I was not sure what these gentlemen did, besides spending enormous sums of money. But, of course, he came home at atrocious hours, weary and bleary eyed, and would then spend most of the following morning in bed. It was a gentleman's life, decadent and pointless. I was happy to have work to keep both hands and mind occupied.

The summer, gentle and fragrant, unfolded in wonders around me, and I delighted in London's generous assortment of parks. The children and I, accompanied by Radha and Sally, the new nanny Geoffrey had hired, would sally forth every day, free to enjoy the mild air and watch the fat little sparrows hop from branch to branch—free from insects, free from snakes and the screeching mischief of monkeys. To me it seemed hard to believe that one could go out-of-doors in all sorts of weather, that no season was so extreme as to hinder the ordinary progression of living. We often took Shadow with us, secured on a leash. He was oddity enough that other nannies, holding the hands of small children or pushing prams, would stop to ask about the little beastie, or simply to admire. It made for some pleasant encounters along our way.

"Servants only," Radha pointed out to me one afternoon as we sat on a stretch of green lawn, watching Winston and Shadow sporting before us. "You see only servants with children. No mothers here."

"There are one or two others," I smiled. "And besides, what difference does that make? I want to be here—not closed up in some stuffy parlor with half a dozen stuffy women, and missing all this."

She smiled back, and I thought for the hundredth time how terribly I would miss her when she went back on the ship. We returned home to a tea of cream and fresh strawberries, and a delicate mint drink that was cool to the taste. English food I found bland and uninteresting compared with the dishes I was used to eating at home. Geoffrey had requested that I teach the cook how to prepare some of our favorites, but often certain ingredients were not easy to find. However, we managed. And each day there was something of interest, and each day Sarah grew. Her eyes grew deeper, her skin more fair, her hair more red hued.

Because of social obligations which Geoffrey took quite

seriously, it became necessary for some new frocks to be made for me. In India we had our own seamstress, but here we must hire such work out, and at what I considered too dear a price. So, on the morning when the girl came for the last of my fittings, I made sure to leave some of my Indian silk and cashmere shawls lying about. They caught her eye at once, as I knew they were bound to. She asked a few subtle questions, which I skillfully encouraged, and in no time at all, we had effected a trade satisfactory to both parties: two large cashmere shawls in exchange for three muslin- and silk-trimmed gowns. The community of retired Indian officers and their ladies were unimpressed by such things as cashmere shawls, but they shone as unexpected luxuries and treasures to those women who would not otherwise have a chance of obtaining them. The bonnets I paid for in cash, but only a fraction of what Geoffrey had thought the cost would be. And I quite shamelessly pocketed the difference in my hidden cache.

At least once a week we met with a group of Geoffrey's friends to drink tea and play whist. He was a good player and often won, sometimes as high a sum as ten pounds. Yet he always bet heavily, and did not seem upset when he lost, any more than he seemed pleased when he won. One evening a new couple was in the party, and I was pleased when I realized that the woman was younger, very close to my age, while all the other ladies were of Geoffrey's vintage, appearing more like mothers to me.

She was a lovely girl, with a canary-sweet voice and the most silken blonde curls. Geoffrey was drawn to blonde women; I had already observed that. And this one was no exception. He made a fuss over her, refilling her teacup and turning the pages of her music while she sang song after song. She was clever as well as pretty, for she could sing in five different languages, and tried nearly all of them out on our patient ears that first night.

I put on the front which most Englishwomen are so skilled at, but I had lost practice of late, and found it difficult to pretend through the whole tedious length of the evening. I mistrusted this woman at best, but did not expect the subtle wound she gave when she glided close to my side and, looking me over with a cock of her dainty head, purred, "So your father married a bubu and you are the result of that union."

She managed to sound as though she were gazing upon some loathsome monstrosity, the undesirable "result" of such a union. I did not favor her with an answer, but turned very coldly away. She giggled lightly as she glided past me. Why did God fashion some women as vipers, striking with deadly, dispassionate accuracy at the very heart of their victims? It was nearly as cruel of Geoffrey to turn on his charms for her, and compromise me when he knew that I had no escape. I had seen it before. I thought of that first night at Dacca when I was so ill and disheartened, and Lieutenant Sheldon had rescued me. If he were here now, I would show Geoffrey a thing or two.

From across the room Emma Miller was watching me. I averted my eyes and began to fumble with the bow at my wrist, which had come untied. She did not approve of Geoffrey's behavior any more than I did. If he were not careful he would lose the respect of these people, and I believe he needed it dreadfully. I had seen other signs—subtle, very subtle. A raised brow, a chance comment, a cold glance from one of the older officers. I settled back into my chair, praying that the hours would, with heaven's mercy, move swiftly and end my ordeal.

Less than a week passed before Geoffrey announced casually that Major Randall was hosting a little soiree and had asked that we might attend.

"Will your singer be there?" I asked. "Flora Daniels?"

"She is not 'my singer,' and I greatly doubt it. He made no mention to me."

"Well, I make mention to you, Geoffrey, that we will in the future find ourselves otherwise engaged, or under the weather when we are invited to any gathering where she also will be present."

He looked at me as though I'd gone mad. We had not discussed at all his infatuation and my discomfort, nay, humiliation, at this woman's hands. Even during the carriage ride home he had chatted gaily about her graces and accomplishments, and I was reminded of something Constance used to often say to me in discussing some couple or other—"A man will take as many liberties as his wife allows him, and treat her just so well or so shabbily as she requires of him."

I had never once dreamed I would need such advice in my own life, but I intended to stick by it now.

"This is absurd," Geoffrey sputtered. "I shall pretend you have not spoken, Charlotte."

"I would strongly advise that you do not. I meant what I said, and I have good grounds to stand on—and what is more, those who would support me . . ." I let my voice trail away. He was canny enough to be concerned about that last statement. He knew that both Colonel Miller and Major Randall, not to mention their wives, thought highly of me. And he knew, as well, that he had suffered a slight falling out with the colonel over some matter to which I was not privy; but he dared hazard no further irritation.

"Well! And if Flora and Oliver Daniels happened to be there tonight?"

"Then we would make some acceptable excuse and leave in very short order."

"Perhaps we had best not go at all."

"Perhaps that would be wise."

He was absolutely fuming. He did not like to be trapped; he did not even like to be thwarted. An hour later he stomped off, sulking, to his club, accompanied by his boy, the ever-present shadow, who had been bribed into spending at least one winter in England before leaving his poor sahib and returning home.

I was not so lucky. Radha left the following Wednesday, sailing with some officers' families who had promised to look after her well. I knew I would never see her again in this life, and despised the powerless feelings that such farewells give. I sent a fat packet of letters back with her, which included one for Dr. Fielding, one for Lieutenant Sheldon—and one for Karan himself. I sent gifts, English tidbits and oddities for Vijaya's larder and herb pots; and books, so difficult to come by in India; jars of jams and tins of biscuits; lots of small, silly things.

She was glad to be leaving, going home, so the parting was not so painful for her as for us. I felt a stubborn sense of desertion during those first days without her. It seemed all traces of the old life had fled, all real ties with India. I had my things, my little treasures, I had Shadow; I now had even a smattering of good Indian food. But the sense of loss persisted, and the melancholy it drew from me. Melancholy, and a strange, gnawing fear.

On the Monday following I found a calling card in my post, and the name scrawled across it in a fine hand sent a cold trembling all through me. I tore it into small pieces and threw it away. The Thursday next an invitation arrived by messenger, begging the pleasure of my company at a late afternoon tea Mrs. Daniels was hosting, and would I be so kind, etc., etc. I sent the footman back with a curt verbal reply only, though I knew it would be construed as an insult. But perhaps that was what was needed to get my message across.

I expected no repercussions, and was astounded three days later to be confronted by Geoffrey himself.

"You have snubbed her," he raged, "on more than one occasion. Now you offer her an insufferable social insult."

"There are no rules of the game which say I must receive her socially," I defended. "I may select my own friends, women with whom I am compatible. I will not be considered untoward, Geoffrey. Emma Miller does not approve of her one little bit."

I was bluffing, but he did not know that. I held my breath and stared him down.

"I did not think you would learn how to be a London snob quite so quickly," he replied, and his tone was so acid that I felt my lips begin to quiver, and had to bite hard against them.

"That is not what it is, and you know it. It is of no importance, Geoffrey! Cannot we simply let the matter end here—or would you rather I question you concerning your knowledge of my actions where Flora Daniels is concerned?"

He was not quick enough to contrive a cover; I had angered him too much for that.

"You try questioning me, my girl, about any of my affairs, and you'll find out you've bit off more than you can chew!"

He did not growl out the words, but spoke them with a calm, almost cordial coldness, which was much harder to bear. *He has lost all love for me,* I thought. It was as though he sensed that I had no friend, no ally, and, like one of the big cats of the jungle, he began to reveal his sharp claws.

I had less guile than he. He brooded on the wrong I had done him and found every means he could to repay me, from petty criticism in front of the servants to thoughtless forgetfulness when I asked him to bring some item home to me from the markets or shops, and then simply ignoring me—pretending he had not heard me when I asked him a question or spoke some light, conversational comment. Only that in the beginning. Then he became a bit careless, coming home later and later, leaving whenever he felt like it, without saying a word to me. His sloppiness extended to the frequent missing of meals, and rude comments spoken in front of the servants, so that I began to be glad to see the back of him, and breathed with relief when I knew I would not have to confront him or put up with one of his dark, ugly moods.

He lived unto himself, even more than in India. But there, I had been *home.* I was still a stranger here, and each day I felt it more keenly, and each day the loneliness ate a little more of me, like the fat black ship's rats that had nibbled at our breads and our cheese. And each day the fear, black and foul as at Dacca, etched its powerful shadow across my heart.

Chapter Twenty-One

Conditions worsened, though I looked for signs to the contrary and spent much energy convincing myself that things were all right, that this spell of selfish indulgence would wear itself out and Geoffrey would emerge from it, restored to himself again. Somehow.

I did not convince myself, though I spent all that energy trying. The summer, hot now on the pavements and in the narrow alleyways between houses, wore itself slowly away. Invitations began to diminish noticeably, then became only a trickle. But so many of the people with whom Geoffrey was acquainted were monied and spent their summer holidays on the continent, or taking in the baths in the south of England. That particular sign could mean nothing at all. There were none of the promised journeys for us. Money was tight, and Geoffrey was even more tight-lipped concerning it. I did not know if opium still figured into his activities, or even into his investments. I did know that his skin was gray hued, and his ruined health was not taking kindly to the punishing routine of his days. If there were women in his life, if he went places of an evening besides his club, if his little warbler serenaded him, I did not know. I knew only that, in the narrow prison of my own days, I was going quite mad.

Some mornings I overcame the pressing gloom of my spirits and took Winston and the baby for an Italian ice in Hyde

Park and a nice walk by the Serpentine Pond. Poor child. Often on such occasions he would unburden his own soul to me.

"I miss the elephants. There is nothing to do here, and nothing to see. No monkeys or mongeese, or lizards. I wonder how Mischief is faring."

"Write and ask."

We had left the pet monkey with one of the regiment children. The men had been assigned to Agra, a pleasant location. "Mischief ought to do well. He's likeable enough, for a monkey."

"You do not like him at all."

"No, I do not," I would reply, and then we would laugh together, and for a few moments things would be all right because we had made them so.

Winston never asked concerning his father, but his serious nature missed little, and one day he said—out of the clear blue, as children are wont to—"I am sorry that my father always makes you so sad. He ought to be kinder and take better care of us."

"He does the best he is able."

"Oh no, he does not. *You* do the best you are able. I don't believe he tries at all."

"Nevertheless, we must love him and pray for him."

"Must we?"

I realized with a jolt that this boy knew nothing about religion. I had neglected the guidance of the most precious thing about him: his little soul.

Several days later, as soon as I could make occasion to do so, I spoke to my husband concerning the welfare of his son.

"There is a fine chapel near here," I told him. "Church of England. I believe we should start taking him to the services."

"You would be bored to tears, my dear. So what do you expect it to do for the boy?"

I tried another request, though it proved just as fruitless. "I should like very much to have a horse. I miss riding, and could use the exercise. There are many riding trails throughout London."

"A horse is too costly."

"When we sold Cinnamon for such a good price you promised me another."

"Well, not yet, Lottie. Not yet."

There was no getting through to him. As the last of the summer burned itself out, as the last roses faded, I spent my days caring for the house and the children, and my evenings either sewing or reading. A sedentary life for a girl of twenty. Sarah Elizabeth was crawling now and talking in that nonsensical baby language which has strains of laughter woven through it. She was Winston's delight and mine also. One rare morning Geoffrey found us all three together in the front hall as he marched through to make his departure, and was forced to slow his steps and observe for a few moments the sheer joy of the scene.

"She is a beauty, Lottie," he murmured.

"Your uncle ought to see her. Have you thought of contacting your family?" I smiled across at Winston. "You have a very handsome son to show off to them, as well as this prattling beauty."

His scowl reached out to each of us. With a few colorful oaths he cursed the very thought of his uncle, and continued his mutterings as he stormed out the door.

"Is Father angry with us?" Winston asked, looking, for the moment, as childlike and distressed as Sarah.

"No, but I do believe he must have had a falling out of some sort with his uncle in order to hold such a venomous opinion of him."

I had said the words without thinking. I did not wish to worry Winston. I placed my hand on his head.

"Never fear, my dear. We shall take care of each other, as we did in India."

"I want to go back home," he said, his blue eyes stirring into a pout like the troubled surface of water.

"So do I. But we are in England, and so must make the best of it. Just think, Winston. The monsoons would be raging right now. The mosquitoes and fleas would be terrible. And the dust. Remember the dust at Dacca?"

He nodded his head. He remembered too well and too much. A child's life should be happiness; my own girlhood had held more simple, gentle pleasures than his young life had known. I pulled him to me and held him tenderly against me. "I love you so much," I said. "I thank heaven for you, Winston, every day of my life."

He did not know my meaning; I could see in his eyes that he did not. I resolved at that moment that he and I would attend services at the tall Gothic church down the street come Sunday. I could not wait all the boy's life for his father's approval.

But Thursday came before Sunday. Thursday morning Geoffrey walked into my boudoir while I was finishing dressing and sent the servant away.

"I have sublet this house," he said, "for a higher rent than we are paying. The movers will be coming on Saturday."

"And where are we going?" I hated how my heart leaped on such occasions of crisis and my whole chest tightened with pain.

"I have taken some rooms in Whitechapel."

"Whitechapel!" Even I knew what a step down Whitechapel was. "What is going on, Geoffrey? It is time you confided in me."

"I've suffered some financial reversals, that's all. Made some unwise investments—though I thought they were canny moves at the moment." His eyes were dark. Even the lines of his face looked tormented, and his skin was still tinged that sallow, unhealthy shade. "We'll get on our feet again." He tried to say the words with spirit, but did not succeed at all. "Only a matter of time." He began pacing back and forth, rubbing his hands in a nervous gesture.

"We shall need some help from you. Things must be packed. You might take Winston out and explain things to him a bit, man to man."

He raised an eyebrow, but did not cease his pacing.

"Winston could use your companionship."

"He never had my companionship in India."

"The boy has been through much," I persisted. "And he is

getting older. He needs the influence of a man—he needs an example . . ."

Geoffrey knew well that I meant, "he needs a *good* example." But he could not fault me, and a head-on confrontation would do him no good at all.

"We shall see," he hedged. "I have my own ends to tie up."

"Business ends," I said, "or social?" It was foolish of me. It gave him an opening, a legitimate reason to rail at me, to vent the force of his anger and feel justified.

I let him go on, but I was not listening. *Rooms—in Whitechapel!* It was not the social humiliation which grated; that was nothing to me. It was fear of change, fear of this downward spiral which would land us—where? As soon as Geoffrey left I put the staff to work packing the old boxes I had brought from India and had stacked in the cellar. I worked beside them, my sleeves pushed up to my elbows, so busy that I did not have time to think.

The rooms were as bad as I had expected, and they offered Geoffrey an excuse, among other things, to cut expenses even further by letting go half of the staff. It made little difference to him; he had lived almost none of his life here, and he still had his boy and—I strongly suspected—his opium.

I thought once or twice of trying to locate my father's people who I understood lived in Shropshire. But shame always stayed my hand. My father's memory deserved better than I was able to give it right now.

Autumn began with a week of cold weather—heavy frosts in the morning and a thick London fog that chilled right to the bone. I nagged at Geoffrey like a fishwife until he found money for me to buy a warm coat for Winston and one for myself. From where we lived I could hear the hollow blare of the ships' horns pulling into the West India docks. One of the loneliest sounds in the world, a ship's horn. Once or twice Winston and I bundled up and walked down there, leaving the baby with the crisp, proper English nanny. How I longed for the deep, languid eyes of the Indian ayahs! At times I despised the crisp

British efficiency and wondered if the passion in my own soul would dry up in this place.

One morning, after staying out so late that our toes and fingers tingled and stung with the brisk air, Winston and I returned home, breathless and laughing, to find the house darkened and shuttered, and wearing the air of a tomb. Upon hearing us in the hall, Sally scurried out of the nursery with her finger to her mouth.

"Sarah Elizabeth is asleep, ma'am, but Mr. Hillard has come home ill. The doctor is with him right now."

This was grave. I could feel the gravity of it. *This is what Geoffrey has been pushing toward,* my mind said. I sent Winston off with Sally and waited outside the closed bedroom door. When the doctor came out, his expression only served to confirm what I already knew. Yet still, his words, themselves, had a shocking effect on me.

"Your husband has cholera, ma'am, a very serious case, it appears. He is in a weakened condition, and the disease has already taken hold."

Cholera. The infectious disease brought from India which attacks the intestines, depletes body fluid and even body tissue, and can kill in less than a week.

"Very important that he be kept in strict isolation. Everything that touches him must be boiled."

"I understand."

"Have you not little ones, Mrs. Hillard?"

I nodded.

"Yes, well, I would suggest that you leave the care of your husband to this Indian servant of his. No use at all endangering yourself and the children."

"He will do well. He has cared for Geoffrey before."

"Very good, then." He put his hand on my arm and began to steer me toward the sitting room. "You look pale, Mrs. Hillard. Come in here and sit down. I'll give you a list of instructions you must see are followed most carefully. And you had better sleep in the nursery with the children and the nanny while this thing runs its course."

I listened woodenly. I knew all the precautions already, and half a dozen excellent Eastern remedies and treatments which would most likely astonish this man.

After the doctor left I remained in the chair. I could not will my body to movement, and certainly not to purpose. I knew, without questioning it, that Geoffrey would die. A terrible revulsion shook my frame at the thought of anyone ending his life in this way. How many dark choices had brought him to this moment? And yet, only three years ago, what a different man he had been.

My mind moved slowly, stunned as if with a harsh blow. What to do, what to do? I knew nothing of his affairs, but I strongly suspected that he had brought us to the point of financial ruin. I wanted to hate him for his stupidity, nay, his cruelty. But right now fear had me in a grip that left almost no room for hate.

The day wore slowly on. Runjeet came in and out of the sickroom several times, but I spoke with him only once.

"Your master?" I began.

He shook his head solemnly. "Very bad, memsahib, very bad."

I performed the hundred tedious tasks the day demanded, but it was so difficult to concentrate, to discipline my stiff hands to function. I ate a solemn supper with Winston while Sita prattled in her chair beside us. I looked upon my children with horror, as though they were already the pitiable, fatherless creatures they soon were to be.

After Sita was in bed and Cook had left her kitchen, I snuck in with Winston and stirred up a batch of chupattees. How good the warm wheat cakes tasted against our tongues! We ate until our stomachs hurt, then, full and sleepy, lay down together, pulling his down coverlet over both of us.

"This is like in the beginning, Mother," Winston murmured, his voice already slurred with sleep.

I smoothed his thick hair back from his forehead. "I'm never afraid when you're with me, Mother," he said with a yawn.

Shadow curled up at our feet. I closed my eyes. The child's faith in me filled my heart with terror. I felt so hurt and abandoned; I felt little more than a weak child myself. I desperately needed some power to lift and sustain me lest I crumple and fall.

The crisis came four days later when the loss of body fluid and the changes in body chemistry resulted in shock. A strong patient can be brought out of this condition. One who is already weakened and who has abused his body cannot.

It was night. Both the children were sleeping and the house was quite still. A London rain was blowing up from the river. I could hear the ships' foghorns calling like lost souls to each other. *Soon Geoffrey will be one of these,* I thought. *Lost and frightened.* For a moment my aching spirit went out to him, and I wished with all my heart that he would live and grow well. The rain sobbed and tore at the dust-stained windows like sharp fingers scratching. I felt chilled to the bone and tightened my shawl around my shoulders.

This is like Dacca, I thought. *Cold and dismal. Square, ugly rooms that do not belong to me, in a place I know nothing about. And despair almost as dark as in that ghost-ridden place.*

I knew the exact moment, for he cried out, as if in pain. I flew to the door of the room and stood there, trembling and uncertain. At length Runjeet came out. His brown eyes swam in pools of tears.

"My sahib is dead."

"Yes," I said. "I am sorry." I wanted to reach out to him, but did not know how.

I walked back to the sitting room and sat beside the cold fire. *I am now alone in the world,* I thought dully. *What will become of me and my little ones?* It was an academic question only. I could not think. I could not even cry.

I closed my eyes and Karan was there, smiling gently. He was so real that I stayed for a long time in that position, my head bent and submissive, my anguish softened by memory, which was all I had to comfort me now.

Chapter Twenty-two

We did, after all, enter the dark Gothic chapel, and Geoffrey with us, unable to protest this last formal rite. I wondered if he would have wanted no part in this Christian putting away of his body, with hymns and scripture texts to accompany it. I did it less for decency sake and for his memory than I did for his son. I wanted Winston to remember his father thus, with tears and gentle thoughts, and solemn words which he could not quite understand, but could *feel*.

I took money from Geoffrey's pockets and from a little box I found in his dressing table drawer to cover the cost of the burial. I found no other assets, and knew I must talk with his solicitor, though I kept putting it off. Notice had been in the papers, and I expected his friends all to come. I cannot say I was hurt by the poor showing, but my sense of desolation was enhanced when I looked around me and saw so few faces, and even fewer I knew.

It was raining when we walked out into the churchyard to lower him into the ground. Just a fine mist that settled like gleaming dewdrops, like a layer of tears.

He was not ready to meet his maker, I thought, looking down into the grim, muddy cavern where the narrow casket would rest.

"A mighty fortress is our God, A tower of strength ne'er failing. A helper mighty is our God, O'er ills of life prevailing. . . ."

We sang the words, our heads bowed to the soft rain and in respect to the dead. I thought not. Respect to death itself, rather. Respect to the proud and powerful messenger whom no man can resist. *Where has he gone?* I thought. *Does his soul live on somewhere? Can he look down on us here? Or is he as disinterested in death as he had been in life?*

"I am the resurrection and the life. He that believeth in me . . ."

How many times had the minister spoken those words to rows of solemn-faced listeners? What did they mean? "He that believeth in me . . ." That certainly left out Geoffrey. Or did it? What had he felt in his heart? Was I to judge? Yet certainly, actions reflect the heart's truest feelings. . . .

My head ached. I was weary of thinking, of wondering. I tugged gently at Winston's coat sleeve and turned away from the grave.

"Excuse me, ma'am."

I looked up into the face of a stranger whose brown eyes were tired but kindly. He was gray haired and stoop shouldered, and appeared to be about seventy years old.

"Mrs. Hillard, I am your late husband's uncle, John Hillard. I am pleased to make your acquaintance."

I began to smile, to express the pleasant surprise I was feeling, but some look in his eyes stopped me.

"That is a fine lad you have there," he said, and I knew that he meant it. And I knew that the pity I heard in his voice was for a reason.

"Indeed, he is," I responded. "Winston, would you please wait on the porch for me while I speak with this gentleman?"

Winston's blue eyes clouded over, dark with uncertainty, but he did as I bade him. I walked off a short distance with Mr. Hillard. He placed his hand on my arm.

"I wished to tell you in person how much I regret what has happened," he began. I nodded in acknowledgment. "Men ought not to be allowed to die and leave such messes behind them." He clucked disapprovingly far back in his throat. I put my hand to my stomach, which felt suddenly weak and queasy.

"Nevertheless, I thought you should know that I intend to forgive all Geoffrey's indebtedness. Although the sums he borrowed were substantial, I would not press them upon you, his poor widow, even if you could pay."

I could feel the blood drain from my face. He tightened his hold on my arm to steady me. "Bear up, my dear. You did not know, did you? For the love of heaven . . ." He was truly distressed.

I shook my head. "Better from you, sir, than from a wronged friend, or a stranger." I raised my face and looked slowly about me. "Is that why so few of his friends are here?"

"George," he called out, "some brandy for the lady, and be quick about it." He turned to me, his eyes thick with concern. "I have a flask in the carriage. Only a moment now."

I let him coax a few swallows down my throat, and the warmth of the liquid felt good.

"My dear lady," he said, "do not distress yourself further. None of the gentlemen Geoffrey borrowed from will press you—"

"But the shame of it," I cried.

"Yes, there is that," he agreed. "But it reflects nothing on you."

But it leaves me friendless and without recourse, I thought.

"Sir," I said, leaning closer. "I know nothing, nothing. Was it the opium trade?"

The muscles of Mr. Hillard's face hardened at my distaste in naming particulars. "Yes, that and his personal addiction, and the type of characters with whom he was in consort."

I had made a mistake. His eyes told me clearly that he did not see how my ignorance could extend quite so far. They also said, as clearly as words: I have been generous. But do not push me. Do not embarrass us both by further requests.

Somehow I managed to thank him, to extricate myself with some few shreds of decency and walk to where Winston waited. *God in heaven, what are we to do? What are we to do?* A terror more cold than the wet fog clutched like a hand at my heart. I could not bear Winston's fear, his innocent faith in me. *God in heaven, if you truly exist, please help me,* I prayed in my heart. And I felt it, I felt the strangling hold loosen. I reached for Winston's cold hand. "Let us go home," I said. "Sita and Nanny are waiting."

He wrapped his fingers around mine, and we walked together, slowly, through the thin drizzle of rain.

I moved quickly, while my tenuous resolve still upheld me. The first thing I did was to clear the house of servants. I had already given them notice the day following Geoffrey's death. Their leave-taking was awkward but not especially painful, save for the panic it built. I had never lived a day of my life without servants. I could not even imagine how such an existence might be. I felt as though I were cutting my lifelines one at a time. I kept the nanny and cook a few days longer, and the day after the funeral, I took a cab to the solicitor's office.

It was as bad as I feared. Geoffrey owed tradesmen as well as friends who had lent him money. The last large shipment of opium he invested in had been seized by the government, or so it was said, the solicitor explained to me.

"Dirty business, dirty business, that," he muttered, pulling at his thin, graying mustache. "Some say it was an inside job, made to look like a bust, and the fellows behind it came out smelling like roses, and none the wiser!" He rubbed his hands together. "Crafty lot, they. Course, that leaves those like poor Geoffrey holding the bag, more's the pity."

We went over the oppressive details. Our only assets were the furniture and other household belongings, which would all have to be sold.

"Beyond that, there's nothing more you can do, ma'am, the mister being dead and all. Can't squeeze blood from a turnip, as the old saying goes."

He made my skin crawl, this weaselly little man. After shaking his hand upon leaving, I wiped my moist fingers down the length of my skirt.

"Save out what you need," he had advised. "A bed for yourself and the little 'uns, kitchen utensils, clothes, and the like." I did more. When I wrote out the list of items to be collected for auction, I did not put down the rocker I had brought from Major Reid's, nor the two Indian paintings that hung on the wall, nor my cashmere shawls, nor the small inlaid wood table that had also come from the major's. The solicitor would not have faulted me. He would be certain to take his own fee off the top before what was left over would be parceled off to the rest. Those who had lost money on Geoffrey would be far from compensated by the sale of our belongings, which, in turn, would devastate us. So goes the world. So go the affairs of men, in which their wives have no part, save the bearing up and the suffering, when it comes down to that.

Before returning to our rented apartment I asked the cabbie to take me to a low-rent district, but one that was still decent and clean. He looked at me as if I were a bit mad, but drove me over the Thames to Lambeth, where I paid the driver his shillings and got out. Then I began walking the streets, looking for something more in keeping with our reduced means where the children and I might live.

I found two rooms on Nine Elms Lane, a subdivision of a larger apartment in a house containing several such units, and I could not guess how many occupants in all. Our rooms would cost only five shillings a week. I could manage that. But I must husband my precious hoard of money until I could figure out some means of bringing in more. What could I do—and do well enough to be paid for? Sketch and sew? But not with polished skill. I could either take in laundry or go into service myself. I cringed at the thought. How could I be a servant to others? I, who had commanded dozens of servants, who had never turned my head without three or four agents appearing beside me, waiting to do my bidding. And what would I do with my children? I could not leave them alone in some squalid room while I went out to earn money.

I had saved the receipts for making my Indian dishes, and a few English receipts I had wheedled from Cook before she left us. And I had salvaged some of the books, part of Geoffrey's vast library which had already been decimated when we were forced to leave India. There were still dozens of titles to go to the auctioneer; no one would miss these. But I prized them like old friends. They would be company during my long nights alone. Shorn of comfort and beauty, and that rarest of all things, British dignity, I would yet have on their pages the thoughts and feelings of great souls who had passed through time, like myself, and whose lives were as lamps to the rest of us, to show us the way.

I worked frenetically, from the early, ashen hours of my mornings until well after dark. I had no time to think, no time to give in to the terror that loomed like a beast on my back. Not until we had landed, like birds of the air shorn of our homing ground, looking for some spot to nest, not until then did awareness wash over me, like the black waves of the sea, or the jaundiced, nasty-smelling fog from the Thames that choked the London streets and alleyways.

Then I sat shivering and wretched, with no will to move at all. Winston would sit beside me, his sea-blue eyes boring holes right through me, but he said never a word. When Sita cried he would get up and take care of her. Then, after a few minutes, or an hour, he would return to my side. I was acutely aware of him, but all else blurred into a dim, meaningless pattern. I did not sleep or eat. I remember refusing the bowls of pale soup Winston offered me. I remember my eyes burning like dry, hot coals in their sockets. I remember my fingers twisting and winding the chain with its smooth gold ring that rested against my throat, twisting it tighter and tighter until the sharp coils of twined gold bit into my flesh.

I sat thus for hours, perhaps a day, perhaps longer. I had no concept of time, no concept of anything except Winston's presence beside me. I did not know what happened, what made the difference. Suddenly I lifted my head and stared back at the child's relentless vigil.

"I am hungry, Winston," I said.

"I will bring you some soup." He was on his feet as he spoke. Then he sat cross-legged at my feet and watched me slurp up the food.

"You will feel better now," he pronounced, taking the empty bowl from me.

I let him tend to my needs, as if I were the child. Not until later, much later that evening when we cuddled together—when I had washed days of neglect from Sita's little body and put her safely in bed—not until then did he say against my hair, "I did what you told me, Mother. I prayed to God."

I sucked in my breath, and when I did not respond he continued.

"I was so frightened!" His thin body trembled. "And then I remembered. And once I started to pray, I could feel someone near me, I could feel someone watching over you. Do you think it was angels?" he asked.

"I do not see why not," I replied, the thought forming slowly. "If there were demons and ghosts in Dacca, I do not know why there could not be angels and guardian spirits here."

He was content. He slept in my arms, as innocent as the baby in her cradle; but his was a hard-won innocence, and blessed of heaven. I could feel that benediction like an aura around us, and I, too, slept.

Chapter Twenty-three

Oh, but it was cold that autumn! The wet fogs would set in and sometimes not lift for days. It would have been nice to take the children to the parks, but I seldom had the heart for it. The first few weeks I spent raising blisters on my hands with scrubbing and cleaning I was not accustomed to, and burning my fingers as I learned to control the heat of the oven as it varied from dish to dish. I did not altogether mind it. I enjoyed continuous contact with the children, and the feeling of being constantly busy and useful. But I had not one whit of freedom. Though my conditions had varied widely over the past few years, they had always included an inordinate amount of time whose use was my own to determine. I might have felt lonely and neglected, but I could still walk in the gardens or take brisk rides on Cinnamon, entertain other wives or young officers, or simply sketch and write letters and fritter my hours away. Now I found myself nodding over my books when I finally got around to them, too tired to keep my eyes open.

I had work in plenty right here, but I had not found a means of employment to supplement my depleted resources. As soon as I had secured this place and had an address to list, I had placed an advertisement in the *Times*, attempting to contact my father's people, listing his name and rank, time and place of death, and saying simply that the daughter of the above would be most grateful for information regarding her unknown family, please respond to such and such an address, etc., etc. I suppose I did not really hope. But sometimes, late at night, when sleep was tardy in coming, I would allow myself the dangerous pastime of pretending. I had done that only one time before, during those torturous months in Dacca. But I was too weak to resist. And how lovely the dreams were, of a tender family who embraced me, and were delighted to find me and restore me to the dignity and splendor of their fine old ways.

But reality persisted. My birthday came on a day of rain and leaden skies. I tried to bake a cake, but ended up scorching it. So I went out for flowers, but found only a few wilted orange mums. *Twenty-one years old today,* I thought. Three years ago—three eternities ago—when I had turned eighteen, a handsome young Sikh had pledged his love to me—had kissed my lips with such tenderness. . . .

I pushed the door open with an almost savage gesture. I was cold and empty-handed, and had no cheer to share with my children, no laughter, no hope.

"Shut the bloomin' door, or you'll let enough fog in to put out the fire."

I blinked at the young woman who had spoken and stood facing me, red cheeked, her blue eyes twinkling, and her hands on her hips.

"This is Emmer from next door," Winston said, unconsciously mimicking her Cockney accent. "She came over to meet us, and I told her it was your birthday, and she's—"

"Hush, lad," she clucked at him. "You'll go and spoil the surprise."

She winked at me. "Emma Simpson. Happy to make your acquaintance, ma'am. Charlotte, isn't it?"

"Lottie. You may call me Lottie," I said.

"Nineteen you are, and not a day older!" She shook a stout red finger at me. "And not used to the life you're livin' here, I'll warrant." She cocked her head thoughtfully. "You look like one of them Indian princesses, all dark-eyed and exotic-like."

I could not help grinning back at her. "I am as British as

you," I returned gaily. "And I turn twenty-one today, which perhaps makes me older than you."

She laughed approval, and her simple good will reached out to me and drew tears to my eyes.

"None of that snifflin'," she scolded. "You just take your hat and coat off, an' I'll be back in a jiffy with some hot scones and plum jam."

In a flash Emma was out the door and disappeared through another.

"She's something, don't you think? She said a birthday tea was just what the doctor ordered." Winston smiled. "Do you think God sent her to us?"

"Have you been praying again, Winston?" I half-teased, to cover the depth of my reaction to him. "I suppose Emmer is just the kind of person God would think of sending our way."

But it was true. She was indeed a godsend during those dark, groping days. She was of a class of people I had never known before, who had been hard used by life from the beginning, and expected nothing better. Nor did they seem to resent those classes above them who enjoyed so many more luxuries and privileges than they.

"Can't miss what you've not had," she was always saying.

But, of course, that was it. I *had* known better. I knew what it was I was missing, and much of my misery came from that fact. She seemed to understand this, and made constant allowances for me, fussing over me as I fussed over Winston and Sita, saving choice tidbits for me, building up the fire while I rocked the baby, washing up the dishes so that Winston and I, sharing the drying, could sing our little nursery songs to her.

She lived with her husband and her ailing father-in-law. There had been no children yet. Although her young man worked scarcely one day in seven, she maintained a cheerful faith in him.

"If my lad could only get something steady-like we'd be happy enough," she would say. "This want of work is hard on a good man what tries his best."

I was not sure I agreed with her assessment of James, but I held my peace on that point. The rooms she lived in were clean and well cared for, with a smattering of family portraits hung on the walls, rag carpets on the floor, and a caged canary named Tatters in one of the kitchen corners who sang at life as smartly as Emma herself.

Winston often slipped over there to hear the pretty bird sing, and sometimes he took Shadow, carefully tied on a lead. The old man, toothless and nearly sightless, liked both the child and the strange little beastie. And it was good for Winston to associate with someone besides myself. He was nearing the age when he ought to begin his schooling. A panic rose in me at the thought of it. I must find some means! Emma was a skilled lace maker, working at home with her pillow, bobbins, and pins. She earned from two shillings to half a crown per yard for her black silk broad lace, and she had offered to teach me. But could I learn? It was difficult, tedious work. Even if I could get the hang of it, my fingers would never move with the sure speed of hers. Speed would be essential—and yards and yards of fine lace sold to earn the kind of money I needed.

I did find work of a sort. Mrs. Jones, who owned the house, hired extra help on washing and ironing days, which meant a minimum of six days guaranteed monthly, perhaps eight or ten. It was grueling work, and I was not used to it, but I pushed those considerations aside. Perhaps someone would rescue me; I still dreamed of the possibility. This was life to Emma—it could not be *Life* to my children and me!

One afternoon I was struggling home with a small bundle of firewood and one or two other parcels tucked under my arm. It was later than I liked, but wood ends and bits sell more cheaply at the closing of market, and I guarded jealously every penny I spent. The fog was so thick that I could see only a few steps ahead of me, and though I picked my way carefully, I stumbled over a protruding stone in the street and felt the wood pieces slide from my grasp.

At that same moment strong arms grabbed my shoulders

to prevent me from falling. As I righted myself my helper bent over and scooped up the sticks of wood from the cobblestones where they had scattered. He was a young man who wore the square, flattened hat of a workman and a loose, short jacket, worn at the elbows and rather faded.

"Thank you," I smiled as he straightened with the wood in his arms.

"Happy to be of service," he answered. "Do you have far yet to go?"

"Only a little distance, to Nine Elms Lane."

"Then allow me to help you."

I looked about me, hesitating. I came this way every day. There were no homes along this stretch, only places of business. My eyes fell upon a lighted hall just down from where we were standing.

"Yes, I am due there for a meeting in ten minutes. But I shall have time." He juggled the wood, readjusting the load a little, and thrust out his hand.

"Seth Taylor from Bath," he said, "just recently come up to London. You are not from these parts yourself."

"No." He began walking in long strides, and I followed him.

"You have the voice of a morning dove, low and soothing, and sweet to the ear."

"And you are a poet come to peddle your wares to silly maidens," I retorted without thinking. But he laughed aloud at my rudeness.

"I did not mean to offend you," he said. "But you are quite beautiful, and quite exotic."

"Am I? I do not feel either," I said.

He was still then, but his gray eyes watched me carefully. When we reached my door he wanted to carry his burden all the way up the long stairs for me, but I would have none of it. I thanked him politely and watched as he whistled back the way that he came.

A great fool I am, I thought, *that a stranger's light words could warm me.*

After I had put away my purchases and greeted the children, I went to stand before the mirror, pocked and imperfect as it was, and examined my features. My eyes were still what I called a wet brown, but there were no lights in them, and my skin appeared sallow, with dark circles under my eyes. I loosened the comb from my hair and shook it about my shoulders. It felt thick and heavy against my fingers, and the strands still gleamed with burnished streaks the shade of live coals. My hair would always be my strong feature, though Constance had often told me what a slender and elegant neck I had. *Constance!* How she would gloat—or at least condescend—if she saw me now.

I choked back a sob. My fingers still played at my elegant neck, at the ring which sat so lightly against my skin. Had I been pretty when Karan gave it to me? I closed my eyes, trying hard to remember, trembling with the effort to restore those lost sensations. But they would not come back. At length I pinned my hair at the nape of my neck and walked into the kitchen to quiet the baby and find something to cook for our supper, something that might disperse the terrible chill that had settled into my bones.

Over the next few weeks I saw Seth Taylor several times. He always had a wave and a smile, and his friendliness lifted my spirit. I experienced no associations in my life beyond the children and Emma, and the other drudges I did laundry with, if they could count. Winter was settling over the city in earnest now. *If I can make it until spring,* I thought, *perhaps we can move to some village. I would not care how poor it is. At least we would have the open blue sky and meadow birds to serenade us, and the sensation of grass at our feet.* I missed the gardens of India. I missed the great trees and the broad, winding waterways. December there was a cool, mild month, free of fleas and mosquitoes and whirling eddies of blinding sand. It was easy to forget the obnoxious and unbearable under the spell of nostalgia. I missed the smells of India, the sounds of her people, the ancient song of chants and prayers coming from mosque and temple. I missed the solemn stillness of sunrise, when the animal world was just stirred, and there was nothing to hurt or to make an alarm. London was stifling and narrow, especially this London I lived in. Even the poor and empty eyed here were not my poor. There was nothing sacred or mysterious about life here, nothing to respect, nothing to which one paid homage, save power and wealth.

I thought of Winston's prayers and berated myself again for my neglect of him. I had no grasp on our lives. Like the rest of London I was merely scrambling and struggling to get by one day at a time. Perhaps that, after all, was what I resented the most.

I had no letters from India, I did not receive a response to my *Times* advertisement. I was adrift and alone. It might take months longer for anything from India to find me, but I chafed at the lack of response to my advertisement, and, scraping together a few pennies, placed it in the newspaper again.

One day early in December I was scurrying home at dusk and nearly ran right into Seth Taylor. He had upset the large leather bag he carried, and two or three of his books had spilled out into the mud. I picked one of them up and handed it to him.

"I am obliged," he said, smiling. Then, wiping it along his coat sleeve, he handed it back to me. "Take it, why don't you. I have others."

"Heavens, no. No, I couldn't. Books are too dear."

He nodded in agreement. "This one in particular."

"What is it?" I asked.

"The Book of Mormon."

"I have never heard of it."

"No, you would not have. It is the translation of an ancient record."

"An ancient translation?"

"No, a modern translation by an American prophet named Joseph Smith."

He spoke the words with a reverence I was not accustomed

to hearing. "Do not back away from me, Charlotte Hillard," he said, with a benign warmth to his voice and a sparkle to his eyes that seemed to melt all my fears.

"There are prophets in India," I said. "They are not scorned or questioned, but their words are held dear."

"Yes, well, in England . . ." He lifted a quizzical eyebrow. "Especially American prophets—even American ideas—are looked upon with much distaste here."

"Why is that?" I asked.

"You can understand, India being a possession, a chattel of Britain. Do you know aught of America's history?"

"A little," I said. "She presumed to do what no one else has ever done."

"Exactly! She was England's colony, and now she stands her equal—but with a vastly greater potential in land and natural wealth."

"So America is the errant child. England dare not recognize anything she might do as superior—"

"Or even up to snuff." His gray eyes softened. "That is pretty much the way of it."

"Then why are you here?" I laughed out loud at my own question. "You are English," I said. "Though you have been speaking as though you, too, are American."

"In some ways I am. I've a favorite uncle who moved his family to Massachusetts. He has prospered exceedingly, and he speaks well of the land and its ways."

"But that is not all." I have enough Indian blood in me to discern beneath the surface. "This religion has intrigued you. It has touched you deeply."

"Yes," he admitted.

He still held his book out to me. "Please take it," he said. "It can do no harm."

I touched it with the tips of my fingers. The leather felt warm to my touch.

"You look as though you are in need of the words of a prophet," Seth Taylor said, and his words fell upon my spirit like the words of a prayer.

I slipped the volume quickly into the depths of my satchel, where it slid beneath the turnips and parsley, safely out of my sight.

Later that week I was out shopping with Emma. As we passed the building where Seth Taylor attended his meetings, I thought to ask her about it.

"You've run into a Mormon? Stay away from the likes of them!" she cried, rolling her eyes like a frightened dray horse. "They're after your soul."

I controlled the urge to smile. "Is not the Church of England after our souls, Emma?"

"Not in the same way they are."

"What are the differences?"

She was becoming vexed with me. "I haven't a head like yours," she muttered, "an' well ye know it. But, I tell you, stay out of their way! I've a brother over in Preston. He says they've made a terrible commotion up there, baptizing people by the dozens, by the hundreds—"

"Baptizing people? Are they not a Christian church? Does not our baptism answer for them?"

"Apparently not!" She snorted triumphantly. "You see, I told you to beware of them."

I smiled and nodded agreeably. Emma would be distraught if she knew she had only heightened my curiosity. My daily life was so dull. What could it hurt to read a translation of ancient scripture? The British looked down their noses at all Eastern forms of religion. What might this one be like? The Book of Mormon—I was glad it still lay tucked in my satchel where I could put my hand on it, if I took a mind to do so, and find out for myself.

Chapter Twenty-Four

I HAD LITTLE CHANCE FOR IDLE occupation during the next weeks. Christmas was approaching, and I was determined to mark the day in some way for my little ones. I possessed a small ivory elephant which had been mine since childhood; I intended to give it to Winston, since he missed the great animals so. That and one or two books from his father's collection, signed over especially to him. Emma had helped me cut patterns for a toy dog and a toy kitten to sew and then stuff for Sita, something new for her to play with. She was outgrowing all of her clothes, and I was a slow, rather clumsy seamstress. Here again Emma helped me cut down and make over some of my dresses for her. I did not need all I had. Certainly the few fine, rather elegant ones Geoffrey had insisted be made for party frocks were of no possible use to me now.

As the bitter winds blew in off the river I often thought of him, buried in the damp, sunless churchyard. Did he rest where he lay? Or worse, was his soul in rest wherever it had fled to? Terrible demons of doubt and wondering sometimes possessed me during the cold midnight hours when I lay staring and open-eyed, alone with the night.

One week to the day before Christmas, Winston crossed the hall between our rooms and Emma's and, bending to pick up some shiny object he spotted, let go of Shadow's leash. The little squirrel immediately scurried away from him, bent on adventure, his nose for once following all those enticing smells that came to him each time he and the young master sallied forth.

Winston was frantic. I am glad I was not there to see his wide, frightened eyes. The naughty beastie slid out the back door and was found contentedly half-buried in the garbage dump twenty minutes later. But that was too late. He had already consumed a quantity of soft, spoiled fruit. Within twelve hours he died, convulsed and glassy gazed. I think it broke Winston's heart. And if the truth be known, his death devastated me entirely. But I could not show it. Winston needed me now with some of the old desperation. His mother's death, his father's death, the earlier death of my infant—our reduced circumstances and unhappiness—and now this. All on his shoulders, all he somehow saw as his responsibility.

I could try to patiently talk him out of it, and he would listen to me. But explanations did not touch the source of his suffering, the wellsprings of his fear. Only my love could hope to traverse that torturous journey. Neither of us slept much that night. And the next morning Sita woke up with a fever and a runny nose.

I tried to be brave. I thought of what Vijaya had told me about a person being no more than what he carried inside. I tried to carry the burdens of fear and shame and disappointment for all of us; and I made myself believe that I could. I made plum pudding with Emma and stirred up small Christmas cakes and custards, coming as close to mango brulee as I could get.

I found myself thinking: *I have fallen off the edge of the earth, and no one knows where I am. The letters I sent back with Radha speak nothing of Geoffrey's death and our quick descent into poverty. Dr. Fielding, even Vijaya, would never guess.* This plain Cockney girl with the thick, work-reddened fingers that could fashion such delicate lace was the only person who could really vouch for our existence. And it was Christmas. My heart ached with loneliness. And my baby's cold had grown worse.

Nothing helped until I remembered how Karan had called me an Indian woman and linked my mother's spirit with mine.

This woman of mystery—what great sorrows had rent her—and might claim her still? Even memory could be nothing but a torturous pain for her. How had she lived day to day? What did she think as she walked the dusty byways of India? How did she imagine her child, the half-caste daughter who carried her own rich, daring blood in her veins? How many nights must she have wept to the point of sickness and distraction, her white knuckles pressed to her mouth? How many times had fierce longing burned her body hollow, only to sear it again and again?

Nothing but thoughts of her could help me bear the unbearable as the stores filled with shoppers and the red-nosed hawkers peddled their glittering wares, and the aroma of roasting chestnuts rose from every street corner. And *love.* People huddled beneath love as beneath an umbrella as they scurried from carriage to doorstep, careful to keep their feet dry. And the poor and the hungry of London huddled in the shadows beyond where the warmth of the chestnut carts reached. Sometimes I forgot I was one of them, and stopped to pity their misery at such a gay, hopeful time.

Snow. It is a strange, almost fairylike substance, yet concealing the sharp nails of a naughty elfin beneath its white fluff. The day before Christmas it snowed. It began soon after the last ribbons of rosy dawn light faded from a white sky. It snowed all morning, gathering thickly in grates and hollows. The cart horses shook it from their long manes and smashed it into mush at their feet. The boys slid and played in it, and packed large round balls of it, with their roughed and cold ungloved hands. People called to one another, strangers across the clogged streetways, as though the snow were a great leveler and a tumbler of barriers. Gentlemen dressed in fine coats and top hats stopped to help push a stuck cab and only laughed when they stepped into the slush to their boot tops. I did not understand it at all.

Winston and I went out into it, though I left Sarah Elizabeth pounding against the window in frustration from the safe grasp of Emma's stout arms. I laughed at the feel of it gathering against my eyelashes; cold, melting pricks of ice on my outstretched tongue. I blew puffs of it away—airy and insubstantial as soap flakes—from the tops of carts and hitching posts, and laughed when it blew back into my face. Winston ran in it, jumped where it had been piled into low mounds, then joined a group of young boys who were rolling large, round balls in order to build a snowman. I watched, as fascinated as they, unmindful of the cold that numbed my cheeks and fingertips. When Emma at last called me in and stuck a mug of hot tea into my stiff hands, the boys had pushed bits of coal into the packed snow for eyes, and a turnip end for a nose. One had found an old pipe which they placed at a cocky angle where the snowman's mouth should be. I looked down at Winston and waved. I was altogether happy for a few brief, magical moments.

Emma and her husband were going across the city to spend Christmas day with his sister—riding in a cab with the old father, at the brother-in-law's expense. She would be leaving soon, spending the night there.

"There are children, you see, six of them," she explained, not even aware of the shining that had come into her eyes. "Children for me," she chuckled, "and Christmas cheer for the men folk, and all will be pleased. But I shall bring a present home for you, my man," she told Winston, tweaking his cold cheek with her big, capable fingers. She had confided to me what it would be. A small canary in a cage, like hers.

"Not to replace Shadow," she hastened to make clear, "but just to give him something of his own, dearie, to love."

We sipped our tea and waved to her from the window as the cab pulled away.

"Too bad she won't be here," Winston said under his breath. The baby's skin felt dry and hot wherever my own skin touched it.

"We'll manage without Emmer," I laughed. But I did not feel quite certain. Everything about Emma was big and loud. She filled so many of the silences in our lives, and covered over the sparse spots. Our celebration would be less replete, less alive without her.

An hour after she left, the post arrived, and in it a letter which bore a postmark from somewhere in the midlands of England, unknown to me. I pulled my old chair close to the fire, still feeling chilled by the wet snow, and slit open the envelope. For a moment or two I remained confused; the person who was writing was obviously a stranger to me. I scanned the lines quickly, but as their message began to come through to me I shut my eyes against it and clenched the arms of the chair. It was so cold; the words on the page were so terribly cold.

"Dear Mrs. Hillard," it began. "I am responding to the request you printed in the *Times* in hopes of deterring you from any further efforts or expense to yourself in pursuing hopes of locating family of the late Major Frances Simmons of India."

Could this woman have been more impersonal?

"I am Frances's younger sister and corresponded with him regularly—and intimately—until his untimely death in Burma in 1824. I can say without doubt that Frances Simmons never entered into a legal marriage—never possessed a wife, *or family,* that would be recognized by church, state or family."

I felt suddenly hot all over and put my hand to my head. I would not have thought—I would not have imagined such a vituperative response.

"Whoever you claim to be, it is of no consequence to those of us who knew and mourned my brother and do not wish his loss resurrected in any sordid way."

The insult was more than implied. I wondered how this woman, in her fear and narrowness, pictured me, and quailed before my own imaginings.

"I discourage you from any further attempts to make contact with the Simmons family. No legal rights would be accorded to any persons—even if he or she could prove to be offspring of Frances's. There would be no hope of inheritance, or the least possible advantage that would accrue to you. Therefore, I urge you to abandon your efforts and leave us to a decent and well-deserved peace," etc., etc. She signed herself "Marion Elizabeth Simmons," with a lengthy address following.

I sat stunned. I felt as though someone had struck me, and was relieved that Winston was playing with Sita in the next room. Was this woman telling the truth? Had she really corresponded with my father through all those years—and yet cared nothing for the painful tragedy he had suffered, nothing for the child he had nurtured and loved more than life? I could not imagine it, yet even in my revulsion I felt myself drawn to her: if she were indeed his sister, she knew him when he was young. She could tell stories, draw with her words childhood pictures. How I longed for such treasures, such "sordid resurrections" of that charming young man who had been the god of my childhood! As my mind trembled with incredulity a thought came to me: perhaps . . . there was a plausible chance that she had not known! I could imagine my father—knowing his family and wanting to protect them—making that choice. I could imagine him protecting his own almost mystical happiness from any base or cruel criticism—even from misunderstanding.

I refolded the letter and slid it back into the envelope, then tucked it between the pages of the book I had been reading which lay on the floor by my chair.

"A fine ending to that fairy tale," I muttered. I felt stupid and foolish, and the venom in the letter reached out to me. *Could she have not waited to send it?* I thought, aware of how pathetic I was, and how pathetic I would appear if someone like my father's well-bred sister could peek in at me now. *It is Christmas!* my heart cried. *There should at least be mercy at Christmastime.*

I was nothing to her. She did not consider me a person with needs such as herself. I was unclean, unworthy in her eyes—*unwanted.* The enormous weight of that fact pressed upon me, until the thought came, unbidden: *So it is in India for those people the British call servants—for those you used yourself, with no feelings at all.*

I did not wish to understand! I made an angry sound far back in my throat. I did not wish to be one of many—the injustice of my life was so *personal,* so all-encompassing, and with every cell of my being I longed for sympathy and release.

I tried to put the mood of the letter behind me as we planned our night's celebrations. But Winston sensed something, and drew even nearer to me, his spirit reaching for mine. At last I felt ashamed. I had this incredible child as my own, and I had his devotion. Why could I not be grateful for that?

We stuffed ourselves with the rich Christmas foods I had prepared and gaily popped our Christmas crackers and donned the paper hats that come stuffed in them, and felt very properly festive. Sita, however, lay hot and listless during most of the evening. I put her to bed before playing games with Winston and then reading the Christmas story from the Bible. His blue eyes grew dark and serious.

"Did it really happen that way?" he asked.

I had no sure answers for him. I had never before lied or demurred from answering any questions he brought to me. "I am not certain," I said. "Great prophets exist in nearly every culture and religion. Some of them claim to be God—or God sent, in one way or another."

"Maybe they're all the same story," he replied thoughtfully, "just told different ways."

I stared at him. I had never thought of that. "You could be right," I conceded. "But then, some view of him must be the most accurate—some belief or truths more pure than others."

He cuddled next to me. "I like this one," he said. "I like Jesus born in a manger." He sighed. "Can we sing Christmas carols?"

At first our voices sounded thin and inconsequential in the stillness. But soon, I forgot their frailty, my spirit soaring on the music and the sense of the words: "Hail, the heav'n-born Prince of Peace! Hail! the Son of Righteousness! Light and life to all he brings, ris'n with healing in his wings . . ."

Light and life to all . . . and power to heal every human heart. That was a godlike characteristic I could scarcely imagine. If one believed—really believed—would that make a difference?

"Oh come, all ye faithful, joyful and triumphant! Oh come ye, Oh come ye . . ."

How does one come to God? How does one feel that joy?

I lay awake for a long time after Winston peacefully slept. The hopelessness I did not want to give way to hovered above my head, like the wings of dark angels that mocked, with no mercy. Sometime after two o'clock in the morning Sarah woke up coughing. I lifted her out of her bed and walked the floor with her, but I could not get her to stop. It was obvious she was in pain. I placed cool cloths against her skin and worked a teaspoonful of warm honey and vinegar down her poor little throat. But she showed no signs of relief.

The cold was bitter. I disliked snow if it did this. Even on the insides of the thin panes of glass at our windows was etched a layer of ice. Sita fretted and began to cough up a brownish-red phlegm. Her breathing became difficult, and obviously painful.

Pneumonia, I thought. *My baby has pneumonia and will certainly die.* For one clear, searing moment I looked the possibility square in the face. *Let her die,* I thought. *Perhaps that is best for her. What life can I give to her here?* And with that thought, a blackness seemed to engulf me and a weakness attack my whole system. And I was afraid.

I ran back to awaken Winston. The first streaks of white light were stretching like bands over the dark sky, thinning the black into gray. Soon the gray would turn white, with perhaps a slight glow of crimson to mark the birth of the day. I thought not of the Savior's birth, but of the birth of this baby, on the heaving gray breast of the ocean—and what joy she had brought into my heart.

I nearly stumbled over the child. He knelt at the foot of the bed in an attitude of prayer. I wanted to wrench him up and shake him out of his calm dreamworld.

"Come! I need your help," I said sharply. "At once!"

He followed me back to the kitchen and picked up his sister, but she moaned in pain at his touch. We built up the fire and placed her little bed near to it.

"As soon as it is fairly light," I told Winston, "I can go for a doctor." *If one will come,* I thought. *If he will take what pay I can offer him.*

That last hour before dawn was a narrow cage of darkness and terror. We bathed Sarah's hot skin and massaged her throat—fearing a dozen times that the last wheezing breath she drew raggedly would be her final one.

How soon dare I leave? I thought, eyeing the door with longing. *If only Emma were here.*

The knock—an urgent, repeated staccato—froze my senses. It came again. I stared at the now-offending door.

"Answer it, Mother," Winston whispered.

"Who in the world could be knocking at our door?" I said.

"Mrs. Hillard—Charlotte Hillard—are you in there?"

I thought I recognized the muffled voice.

"It is your friend—Seth Taylor—I have come to help you!"

My friend. He thought of himself as my friend.

"Let me in. Please."

I stumbled to the door and unlatched it. He stood framed in the doorway, so sane, so everyday looking. He had another young man with him.

"This is Brother Lewis," he said. "We have come to help you."

"How did you know I needed help?"

Seth Taylor smiled, and his gray eyes grew soft as the morning. "I felt it," he said simply. "I woke up twice in the night, then again about an hour ago. Each time I had the strongest impression that you needed me—needed help."

He extended his arms, as though somehow yearning toward me, and I thought of Dr. Fielding.

"The feeling grew so urgent that at last I woke Graham here and told him he must come with me."

"My baby daughter is ill. Very ill. I believe it is pneumonia. I can scarcely get her to breathe. Could you go for a doctor?"

The young man hesitated. I saw the change in his eyes.

"Sit with Winston then, for heaven's sake," I blurted. "And I shall go for the doctor myself."

"Might we come in for a moment first?" he asked hesitantly. "We have come to help you. We sincerely believe that we can."

"What are you talking about?" I nearly shouted. "My child needs a doctor's care."

Seth Taylor raised his head and held my gaze with his serene eyes. "There are ways of healing—and there are ways of healing," he said. "There are the ways of man, and there is the way ordained of God—the way revealed by his Son."

Something in his words washed over me like a light, some response surged within me. Just then Winston came to the door.

"I prayed for help," he said. "Did God send you to us? He has answered my prayers before."

"I believe he has done so again, young man." Seth Taylor's eyes filled with tears. "May we come in, Charlotte?" he said.

Somewhere in the distance I could hear the Christmas bells ringing—some loud and clamoring, some solemn and deep throated, some light and airy as an angel's chime. All together they sang a hymn of praise to the morning. I smiled into the shining gray eyes.

"If Winston has prayed you here, who am I to interfere, to show the only weak lack of faith?"

The gray eyes smiled in return. *Earth and heaven hold more wonders than I know,* I thought, as I held the door and stood aside for them to pass.

Chapter Twenty-Five

I did not hear bells and the singing of angels, nor see heavenly lights. But I do believe that the faith of childhood can move the powers of heaven, and I was forced to believe those things I did see with my own eyes.

At first I was frightened when Seth Taylor explained what it was he wanted to do.

"You will be right here watching," he encouraged. "We cannot harm the child—and if we do no good . . ." He held his arms out, palms upward. There was an entreaty, calm and confident, about his manner that moved me to give my consent.

I felt *something*—I do not know what I felt. But when they anointed Sita's head and placed their hands upon her—large, sinewy hands, warm with life, upon her burning frailness—closed their eyes, and commenced to call upon the powers of heaven, I felt the rightness of it. There was nothing of the charlatan here, no strange distortions or affectations, nothing exaggerated or even unseemly. When they were done, the two men stepped back. Seth Taylor smiled at me. "She will be all right now. Look how calmly she is sleeping."

It was true. Her ragged breathing had ceased; her tense muscles were relaxed. It even seemed that her forehead did not feel so hot as I pressed my fingers lightly against the white skin.

I did not know what to do. I offered the men refreshment, and to my surprise, they accepted. I should have felt awkward in their presence after the intimacy of what had just happened, but I did not. We conversed easily; Winston was in his element, and the two men behaved with a graciousness which impressed me. The English manners are stiff, with a gloss of the formal no matter what the occasion. The manners of the Indian are gentle, as smooth as an oar moving through still water. These men were different from both, exhibiting a friendliness which bordered on an improper familiarity but was saved, somehow, by the genuine solicitude of their manner, and the fact that they behaved like gentlemen.

They did not stay overlong. Nor did Seth Taylor press me. I kept thinking to myself, *What do I owe these men? What should I say?* After they had risen to leave and were standing by the open door I stammered awkwardly, "I have little to thank you with. Would you like—"

Both men smiled, and my friend laughed softly. "You have as much to thank us with as anyone—full as much soul and heart."

Strange words, I thought. He reached out suddenly and caught up both of my hands. "Allow us to return tomorrow to check on you and the children," he said. "That is all we ask."

I nodded consent; what else could I do, all considered?

He still held my hands in his. Now he looked straight into my eyes. "You carry a burden, Charlotte, a very great burden." I shuddered. His words mirrored the anguish I had been feeling, the complaints of my soul during these last days.

"There is one who would help you, who would happily remove this burden from you."

I shook my head and pulled my hands away from his. "He has already begun to do so," the young man continued, unruffled. "Go in and look again at your child. He whose birth we celebrate this day is the one I speak of."

He did not smile. But his eyes were filled with tenderness as he said good-bye to the both of us and shook Winston's hand. I listened to the clatter on the stairs, then the settling silence. I went in and stood over Sita. Her color was returning; she slept with a soft, even breathing. I stood gazing down upon her a long, long time, until Winston gently tugged me away to see to other concerns.

Emma and her husband must have stayed late at her sister's. I did not hear them come in. But in the gray, cold morning when I awoke, the first thing I heard was a heavenly sound—a sound that transported me to the dry, dusty warmth of India and made my heart weep.

Winston heard, too. He ran to the small cage that swung gaily above our table and pushed a shy finger toward the bright green canary, who blinked back at him and cocked his gold-tufted head.

"You like my gift, lovie?" Emma came out from behind the open door where she had managed to secrete the great bulk of herself. Her face was red with good cheer and pleasure.

Winston clasped his small hands and ran to her. I turned to smile at Sita, who, I suddenly realized, was standing up in her bed, shrieking with pleasure and waving her tiny arms toward the bright bird.

"Look at her, will you? I thought she was coming down ill last time I held her—so listless and hot."

I caught Winston's eye. No good would come of telling Emma what had happened.

"A Christmas miracle," Winston answered. "Jesus made Sita better."

Emma laughed and gave him a great bear hug, and the tense moment passed. But she sat so long over her mug of tea, telling the happenings of her Christmas—the antics of the children, how naughty they were compared with Winston—that I heard with a sense of panic the sound of steps on the stairs. Could a child be as canny as Winston seemed?

"Take me to visit Tatters, please," he cried as he lifted the cage from its hook, "and let him meet his new friend."

Emma was pleased with the idea. She bustled through her own door, pushed gently by Winston, just as my young friend from Bath appeared at the head of the stairs.

"You look glowing, Charlotte!" he cried. "So very—" He paused. I think he meant to say "beautiful," then thought better of it. "Is Sita still well?"

It annoyed me a little, the way he used our familiar names, but I knew he meant no harm by it. I took him in to the child. He had brought her a small piece of hardened maple sugar to suck upon, and he watched her with pleasure as she proceeded to suck and drool happily.

"You must not stay long," I said. "I have a friend—she may reappear any moment—and—"

"And you do not want to have to explain me?" He nodded, but his eyes were thoughtful. "We've a meeting tomorrow," he said. "Will you come?"

"I think not."

"And why?"

"It would not be a wise thing. . . ." I felt myself fidgeting, and ran a finger beneath my warm collar, then smoothed out the apron I wore.

"You've a right," he replied, "to see for yourself what power it is that restored your daughter to health." He paused, perhaps to let his words sink in a little. "You owe nothing to gossipers and dissenters who are unknown to you. But you do owe something to yourself, and to your children—and perhaps even to God."

That was all. He left as bidden, but his words had disturbed me. And that night I dreamed of Karan. In the dream he kept saying, "Do as your heart bids, my sweet Lottie. Follow your heart—has it not always led true?"

And yet, as I slipped out the door the next evening, I was glad for the cloak of darkness that covered me. Earlier I had asked Emma to check in on Winston and Sita, but I did not tell her where I intended to go. I wondered if it was not more my pride, and a sense of duty that sprang from it, that had moved me to do what I was doing. Now my obligation to these people would be settled, and I could get on with my life.

I sat in the back and slid down in the seat, doing all I could to render myself invisible. But as the meeting progressed, as the words found their way to me—words I had never heard before—I straightened, found myself leaning forward as I strained now to hear. The topic was faith, and the elderly man who was addressing the group spoke with such quiet authority.

"Faith is a power," he said, "that connects us to God. We are his children. We have a right to his guidance and counsel as we struggle to be like him—"

Like God? The idea thrilled me. This was a teaching I had never heard before, and it appealed to something within me that before had been untouched. Forbearance and submission—I had been taught this all my life. But *eternal progression*—the chance to become godlike through the things we suffer and learn here!

I tried to slip out at the end, too overwhelmed by what I had heard to face society. But Seth Taylor would not allow it. He introduced me to some of his friends. And I was amazed to feel from them the same acceptance, the same tender solicitude I had been feeling from him.

He insisted on walking me back to my apartment, but we did not really speak as we negotiated our way through the dark, snow-choked street. As he bid me good night, he placed his hand on my arm and said, "You liked what you heard."

"You expected as much?" His words stung me a little.

"Yes, I did. For I had already discerned that you carry truth within you. Light cleaves to light, Charlotte. That is all that happened tonight."

Light cleaves to light. I had so much to think upon! When I slid my key into the lock and pushed the door open to see Winston fast asleep beside the low fire, I felt a half-guilty relief. I was alone. I had the time I needed. I rummaged through my satchel and pulled out the Book of Mormon. Perhaps it was time for this now.

The following morning Emma came over early. She meant to teach me the art of lace making if it took her all day! It was cold still. The weather had not broken since Christmas. And though it had turned gray with the soot and grime of the city, snow still covered the ground.

"I prefer sand," I sighed as I stared out the window.

"I wouldn't know, lovey," Emma chuckled, settling herself into a chair with a groan. "But if that dry sand is kind to the rheumatics, then I'm all for it, too."

I did the best I could, my fingers stiff and moist with perspiration as I attempted to work the many small bobbins of thread around the pegs which Emma had fastened into a pillow along the lines of the design she had drawn.

"I am all thumbs," I complained, "and worse when you watch me. My fingers become thick and unwieldy as sausages as soon as you cast your eye on my work."

She grinned, showing the spoiled, uneven teeth she worried about no more than she did her vast girth. "You'll catch on, lovey, with the head you've got on your shoulders! You see, I figures you can make up some fancy foreign designs from that Indian background of yours—and the rich folk'll start askin' for them—and you'll up and make yourself rich."

I smiled back. I must stick with it for her sake, if not for my own; yet I feared I should never justify her blind faith in me. I kept working steadily away, head bent, eyes squinted painfully, till I heard Emma let out a cry—a howl of surprised anger. I looked up to see her standing over me, hands athwart her wide hips. *What have I done wrong?* I thought, trembling.

"What is this wickedness 'ere?" she demanded, tossing a book into my lap as though it scalded her fingers the way a hot coal would, and barely missing the pattern of pegs which had been so painfully situated.

I looked down. It was the Book of Mormon that lay, spine upward, pages bent and sprawling, across my apron. I picked it up gingerly, as though I, too, feared that my flesh might scorch at the touch.

"What be you thinkin', lovey? What madness is this?"

"A friend gave it to me."

"Friend, is it?" She eyed me with a sudden suspicion. "He be no friend to you if he be a Mormonite, Lottie. He'll bring you nothing but woe."

"Honestly, Emma," I responded, making my voice sound light. "I do not see what the concern is."

She shook her head as she would at a child who had misbehaved and was too dull to see his offense. "Get rid o' this, and get rid of any queer notions you may have in your head."

Winston was watching us. She turned to him and shrugged

her broad shoulders. "Your mother's a babe in the woods, she is. But then, I suppose you know that."

I stuffed the offending book back into my satchel, and Emma let the matter drop, but I knew she remembered it still when she asked me the following evening, "You're not mixed up in any strange doings, are you, love?"

"What do you think, Emma?" I countered.

She muttered under her breath, but her eyes were still wary, and the distrust I saw there wounded me. Why was a man's religion a matter of such interest to his neighbors? Why did men deem it proper to wound, to maim, to kill in the name of religion? Why must this be so?

I cannot say why, not for certain, but the following evening I went to meeting again. I had retrieved the Mormon book and set it discreetly on my table beneath several other volumes, but I had not read in it yet. When Seth Taylor learned this he seemed a bit disappointed, but, as before, he did not press me. The sermon this night was centered on one of the teachings brought forth by this American prophet who was named Joseph Smith.

A common name for a very uncommon man, I thought.

"These are not the words of Joseph," my friend explained, perhaps reading my expression, "but the words of the Savior through him."

"Revelation?"

"Revelation. It has always existed when God's authority and organization have been on the earth."

I did not quite understand, but as I turned my attentions again to the speaker, I understood the words he was saying, both their content and their spirit. They fell like calm, cool stones on the troubled surface of my mind.

"No power or influence can or ought to be maintained by virtue of the priesthood, only by persuasion, by long-suffering, by gentleness and meekness, and by love unfeigned. . . ."

There was nothing of the bigot, the fanatic in those words. Their purity trembled through me. Could it be possible that people misjudged the Mormons?

I allowed Seth Taylor to escort me home again. The discolored snow had turned to black slush at our feet.

"You miss India terribly, don't you? Your other life?" His eyes could not conceal his intense curiosity.

"I am lost here," I replied. "I do not belong in this place, nor in these circumstances."

"No, you do not," he agreed, shaking me from the strange lack of restraint which had allowed me to speak so honestly. "But the purpose for these trials will be revealed to you, and God will take you in hand and provide—" He stopped short. My eyes followed his startled gaze, but before comprehension sank in I felt a sharp tug on my arm and heard Emma's strident voice rasping out orders like a major.

"You get right away from her, you fiend! What has possessed you, Charlotte—being seen with this man? Everyone knows that he's one of those Mormonites. Is it true then, what Winston said? I refused to believe him—but now I have the evidence before my own eyes!"

She was irate; I could do nothing to calm her, though I attempted to speak soothingly and reasonably with her in turn. At last, in frustration, I turned to my escort, who was much distressed by the scene he had caused.

"The day following tomorrow I start a season of work," I began to explain, "and will be absent long hours from my children. So do not expect to see me at meetings for—" I hesitated.

"For?" His expression was quizzical; he was doing his best to conceal the tension in the lines of his face, which betrayed his keen interest.

"For—a while," I finished lamely.

Emma still had hold of me and began dragging me physically up the stairs. Seth Taylor stood with his arms folded, watching after us. I thought I heard him murmur under his breath, "God keep you, Charlotte Hillard." The words followed me like an echo of all that had ever been lovely and good in my life.

I did not look forward to the grueling days of work ahead of me, but our means were perilously depleted, and I was in desperate need of any income I could get. I continued to work persistently each day to master lace-making skills, though my fingers were red and my eyes burned from the hours of close concentration.

The night after Emma's blowup I sat up late with Winston. I had been reading to him, but now he had taken up his toys and was occupying himself. I thought I would just look through this Book of Mormon before bundling us both off to bed. I had scarcely lifted the cover, when the door to my rooms burst open and Mrs. Jones appeared, red-faced and distraught. She snatched the book from my hands and, with a cry of anger, threw it into the fire, where the thin pages sizzled and curled.

"I thought better of you, I did, missus," she said through clenched teeth. "But I'll have no Mormonites here. You've got three days to quit my premises, and there'll be no work for you—not tomorrow, not ever in my house."

She stomped out of the room, leaving Winston and me blinking at each other. I gave him a weak smile that became all trembly and disfigured.

"It will be all right, Mother," he said, coming to stand by my side.

I nodded, unable to answer. But my insides had gone cold. To be evicted from lodgings such as I was in . . . to be reduced to a penniless, homeless state . . . I dared not let myself think of it!

I got ready for bed somehow, not aware of the motions I was going through, stunned yet at the perilous state in which I now found myself. As I approached the bed Winston and I shared I realized that the boy was kneeling on the cold floor, praying. I stood and stared at him stupidly. I stifled an urge to reach over and shake him and shout out at the top of my lungs, "What good will that do?" Instead, I climbed into the bed and huddled miserably until his warm little body cuddled close and comfortingly against mine. He fell asleep almost at once. But I lay shivering and open-eyed through most of the night. I could not pray, I could not even think; I was in a terrified stupor that even morning, when it came gray and sunless, could not dispel.

Chapter Twenty-Six

I HAD NOT SEEN EMMA SINCE OUR encounter on the stairs, and the nagging suspicion ate at me: Was it Emma who had told Mrs. Jones of my association with the Mormons? Would she really do that? As the dreary day progressed and we saw no sign of her, my suspicions deepened into a sickening fear. If Emma had betrayed me I would be friendless and comfortless, as well as destitute.

Yes, I thought of Seth Taylor; I could not avoid it. My panicked need sent my mind searching everywhere. But I shrank at the idea of appealing to him—that would rob me of the very last shred of dignity and self-respect I could cling to, and then, truly, I would not have the strength to go on.

I knew this much. I had means for a few days of feeding myself and the children; no more. I must find work, steady employment, no matter how menial, before I could secure a new place to live. There were poorhouses in London—but I shuddered at the vision I had of them. They seemed as great a nightmare as the haunted house at Dacca, and worse—because they embodied the hopeless nightmares of the living.

In desperation I went out later that day in search of I knew not what. I checked every shop and factory I passed, asking if help was wanted, but from each door I was turned away. Growing more persistent with each rejection, I took a cab to the fashionable heart of London. With more care than usual I had dressed that morning in one of the gowns Geoffrey had insisted I have made for myself, and had wound my great mass of hair in a tidy braid round my head. I felt like a ghost of something garrish and tragic that had perished and left nothing behind it but a sad, empty shell. Now I feared that I had erred, that my manner of attire and deportment was incongruous with the supposed need I was presenting. Whatever the case, no one took pity upon me that day, and when I at last turned my steps homeward my feet were so sore and frozen, my stomach so pinched and my head so light from not eating, that I could feel myself reel and stumble as I struggled along.

The early winter twilight was sifting like soot over the cold, blackened buildings. I felt myself in a vacuum, apart from all humanity. Even the street vendors, hawking their goods, had melted from the sidewalks, and all about me seemed eerie and still. Then a gaggle of crows, squabbling for a roost on the roof lids above me, set up their cry, as hollow and haunting as the black, dusty crows back in India. It was too much to bear. I sank down on the dirty cobbles of a half-deserted alley, hugged my knees to my chest, and began to sob like a child. I could not cry in front of Winston, but here I shuddered out the terrible misery of the past months, the misery that had festered inside for so long.

At last I arose, weaker than before and feeling even more empty. As I approached the dim entrance to the old boardinghouse which would no longer shelter me, it seemed the very boards of the building, in distaste and repudiation, shrank from my touch. And then the large bulk of Emma pushed past me. She was walking head down, beneath the protection of a broad shawl, obviously bent on some purpose. Perhaps she did not notice me, but I doubted it. With a terrible leaden hopelessness I climbed the stairs and entered the room where my children waited for the necessities of sustenance and comfort which I had no way to give.

Enwrapped in this sense of desolation, which was as enfeebling as my weariness and my hunger, I went about the mechanical motions of preparing a meal for the three of us. Winston was unusually quiet. Perhaps he read the despair on my face and could find no defense against it.

I did not hear the knock at the door. I remember only the sound of Emma's voice, the clean, homey smell of her as she bustled into the room.

"See what you've caused!" she bristled. "You be responsible for this! Poor lamb—to think that she has to suffer for your demented, ungodly ways."

She smothered me in her arms, but I caught sight of the man who had come in behind her and stood with an awkward uncertainty regarding the scene before him. Pushing Emma gently aside, I, too, tried to figure out what was happening.

"I went to fetch this heathen myself," Emma announced, half in pride, half in apology.

"I thought you were angry with me. I thought you told Mrs. Jones—"

"Shame on you, honey," she scolded, and her face showed honest hurt. "Do you b'lieve I'd do a mean thing like that?"

"I didn't want to. But I was so frightened—and you ignored us—"

Her face reddened. "I was mad as a hornet," she admitted. "But when I heard what the landlady had the nerve to do to you and the little ones—"

"Well, all that is over now." Seth Taylor stepped forward. "I have made other arrangements."

I blinked at him vaguely. "What in the world do you mean?"

"'Tis not really I," he said, as though upon second thought. "Just this afternoon we received an unusual request from a woman of our acquaintance." He coughed and added, with deliberate emphasis, "A woman of means."

I was staring at him; so was Winston. "Go on, lad," Emma barked, prodding him with a round elbow in his ribs, at which he grinned like a boy.

"Aunt May Skinner is the woman's name," he continued. "She has a large house in Bayswater and is in need of—"

"A servant!" I cried, hope breaking over me like a cold, invigorating wave.

Seth Taylor smiled gently. "She has a full complement of servants. No, she is seeking what she terms 'a companion.' You see, she is elderly, and her eyesight is poor, and she desires someone who can read to her, accompany her to afternoon teas and evening concerts—"

My pulse was beating like a drum at my temples.

"Such a woman—young and of gentle background; she wishes no one coarse or uneducated—such a person is not easy to find. But I sent a note off to her house before coming here, to say that we have found the very person she is looking for."

"What of the children?" I breathed.

His boyish grin became an almost angelic expression of warmth and understanding. "She already specified that she had no objection to children; in fact, she rather welcomed the idea of having a little life and laughter about the house. May is a kindly woman. You will enjoy her company, Charlotte."

I leaned back in my chair, drained of the last vestiges of strength I had held on to.

"Get the child a hot drink!" Emma barked. "She looks about to faint on us."

"An unusual request," Seth Taylor repeated as he handed me the steaming cup Emma had poured. "And coming out of the clear blue, as it did, right at this moment—seems the Lord took you in hand sooner than even I expected."

I closed my eyes, and that Christmas morning came rushing back to me. What was it Seth Taylor had said? *There are the ways of man—and there is the way ordained of God.* Yes, that was it. He had saved us then—or the way of his god had saved us. And now—for a second time . . .

"I have no faith," I said softly, so that he had to lean forward to hear me. "You have faith in your god; so does Winston. But I have none." I shivered as a feeling of shame washed over me.

"You cannot see yourself," he replied quietly, "your incredible courage, your incredible faith." Tears misted his eyes, and it seemed that he choked on the words.

"'Light and life to all he brings . . .'" I whispered. Winston heard me and smiled.

"You are in his hands now, and he will continue to uphold you and show you the way you should go."

Simple words, spoken in such a straightforward manner. But the powerful truth behind them pierced straight to my heart, like the promised light in the song. In a way I could not explain, unaccountable and wonderful, I felt as if I had found my way, as if—after a long, painful absence—I had just come home.